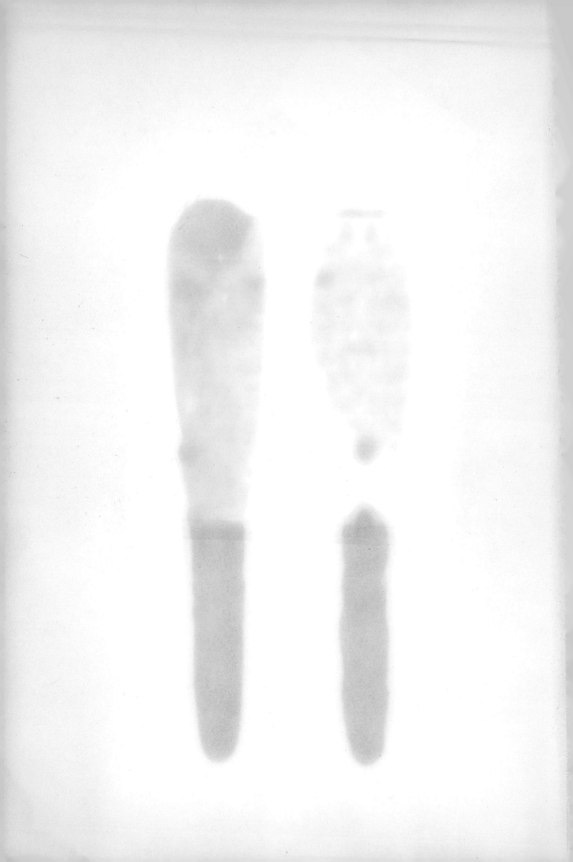

ECONOMETRICS

ECONOMICS HANDBOOK SERIES
SEYMOUR E. HARRIS, Editor

ADVISORY COMMITTEE: Edward H. Chamberlain, Gottfried Haberler, Alvin H. Hansen, Edward S. Mason, and John H. Williams. *All of Harvard University.*

ECONOMETRICS

An Introduction to Maximum Likelihood Methods

STEFAN VALAVANIS

Assistant Professor of Economics
Harvard University, 1956 to 1958

EDITED, FROM MANUSCRIPT, BY
ALFRED H. CONRAD

Assistant Professor of Economics
Harvard University

1959

New York   Toronto   London

McGRAW-HILL BOOK COMPANY, INC.

Editor's introduction

For years many teachers of economics and other professional economists have felt the need of a series of books on economic subjects which is not filled by the usual textbook, nor by the highly technical treatise.

This present series, published under the general title of *Economics Handbook Series*, was planned with these needs in mind. Designed first of all for students, the volumes are useful in the ever-growing field of adult education and also are of interest to the informed general reader.

The volumes present a distillate of accepted theory and practice, without the detailed approach of the technical treatise. Each volume is a unit, standing on its own.

The authors are scholars, each writing on an economic subject on which he is an authority. In this series the author's first task was not to make important contributions to knowledge—although many of them do—but so to present his subject matter that his work as a scholar will carry its maximum influence outside as well as inside the classroom. The time has come to redress the balance between the energies spent on the creation of new ideas and on their dissemination. Economic ideas are unproductive if they do not spread beyond the world of scholars. Popularizers without technical competence, unqualified textbook writers, and sometimes even charlatans control too large a part of the market for economic ideas.

In the classroom the *Economics Handbook Series* will serve, it is hoped, as brief surveys in one-semester courses, as supplementary reading in introductory courses, and in other courses in which the subject is related.

Seymour E. Harris

Editor's preface

The editor welcomes Stefan Valavanis' study of econometrics into the *Economics Handbook Series* as a unique contribution to econometrics and to the teaching of the subject.

Anyone who reads this book will understand the tragedy of the death of Stefan Valavanis. He was brilliant, imaginative, and a first-class scholar and teacher, and his death is a great loss to the world of ideas.

Professor Valavanis had virtually completed his book just before his departure for Europe in the summer of 1958. But, as is always true of a manuscript left with the publisher, though it was essentially complete much remained to be done. My colleague, Professor Alfred H. Conrad, volunteered to finish the job. Unselfishly he put the final touches on the book, went over the manuscript, checked the mathematics, assumed the responsibility for seeing it through the press, and helped in many other ways. Without his help, the problem of publication would have been a serious one. The publisher and editor are indeed grateful.

This book is an introduction to econometrics, that is, to the techniques by which economic theories are brought into contact with the facts. While not in any sense a "cookbook," its orientation is constantly toward the strategy of economic research. Within the field of econometrics, the book is primarily addressed to the problems of estimation rather than to the testing of hypotheses. It is concerned with estimating, from the insufficient information available, the values

vii

or magnitudes of the variables and relationships suggested by economic analysis. The maximum likelihood and limited information techniques are developed from fundamental assumptions and criteria and demonstrated by example; their costs in accuracy and computation are weighed. There are short but careful treatments of identification, instrumental variables, factor analysis, and hypothesis testing. The book proceeds much more by statements of problems and examples than by the development of mathematical proofs.

The main feature of this book is its pedagogical strength. While rigor is not sacrificed and no mathematical or statistical rabbits are pulled out of the author's hat, the statistical tools are always presented in terms of the fundamental limitations and criteria of the real world. Almost every concept is introduced by an example set in this world of real problems and difficulties. Mathematical concepts and notational distinctions are most often handled in clearly set off "digressions." The fundamental notions of probability and matrix algebra are reviewed, but in general it is assumed that the student has already been introduced to determinants and matrices and the elementary properties and processes of differentiation. (No more knowledge of mathematics is required than for any of the other comparable texts, and, thanks to the pedagogical skills of the author, probably considerably less.) Frequent emphasis is placed upon computation design and requirements.

Valavanis' book is brilliantly organized for classroom presentation, most of the statistical and mathematical assumptions and concepts being treated verbally and by example before they appear in any mathematical formulation. In addition to the examples used in presentation, there are exercises in almost every chapter.

Seymour E. Harris

Preface

This work is neither a complete nor a systematic treatment of econometrics. It definitely is not empirical. It has one unifying idea: to reduce to common-sense terms the mathematical statistics on which the theory of econometrics rests.

If anything in econometrics (or in any other field) makes sense, one ought to be able to put it into words. The result may not be so compact as a close-knit mathematical exposition, but it can be, in its own way, just as elegant and clear.

Putting symbols and jargon into words understandable to a wider audience is not the only thing I want to do. I think that watering down a highly refined or a very deep mathematical argument is a useful activity. For instance, if the essence of a problem can be captured by two variables, why tackle n? Or why worry about mathematical continuity, existence, and singularity in a discussion of economic matters, unless these intriguing properties have interesting economic counterparts? We would be misspending effort if all the reader wants is an intelligent layman's idea of what is going on in the field of econometrics. For the sake of the punctilious, I shall give warning every time my heuristic "proof" is not watertight or whenever I slur over an unessential mathematical maze.

Much of econometric literature suffers from overfancy notation. If I judge rightly, many people quake at the sight of every new issue of *Econometrica*. I hope to show them the intuitive good sense that hides behind the mathematical squiggles.

Besides restoring the self-assurance of the ordinary intelligent reader and helping him discriminate between really important developments in econometric method and mere mathematical quibbles, I have tried to be useful to the teachers of econometrics and peripheral subjects by supplying them with material in "pedagogic" form. And lastly, I should like to amuse and surprise the serious or expert econometrician, the connoisseur, by serving him familiar hash in nice new palatable ways but without loss of nutrient substance.

The gaps in this work are intentional. One cannot, from this book alone, learn econometrics from the ground up; one must pick up elementary statistical notions, algebra, a little calculus—even some econometrics—elsewhere.

For the beginner in econometrics, an approximately correct sequence would be the books of BEACH (1957), TINBERGEN (1951), KLEIN (1953), and HOOD (1953); with TINTNER (1942) as a source of examples or museum for the numerous varieties of quantitative techniques in existence. TINBERGEN emphasizes economic policy; KLEIN, the business cycle and macro-economics; TINTNER, the testing of hypotheses and the analysis of time series. All three use interesting empirical examples. For elementary mathematics the first part of BEACH (perhaps also KLEIN, appendix on matrices) is enough. Reference to all these easily available and digestible texts is meant to avoid my repeating what has been said by others.

From time to time, however, I make certain "digressions"; these are held in from the margins. These digressions have to do mostly with mathematical and statistical subjects that in my opinion are either inaccessible or not well explained elsewhere.

Stefan Valavanis

Acknowledgments

Harvard University, for grants from the Joseph H. Clark Bequest and from the Ford Foundation's Small Research Fund in the Department of Economics.

Professor and Mrs. William Jaffé

Professor Arthur S. Goldberger

Professor Richard E. Quandt

Professor Frederick F. Stephan

Contents

Digressions

Frequent references

Names in small capital letters refer to the following works:

ALLEN   R. G. D. Allen, *Mathematical Economics*. New York: St. Martin's Press, Inc., 1956. xvi, 768 pp., illus.

BEACH   Earl F. Beach, *Economic Models: An Exposition*. New York: John Wiley & Sons, Inc., 1957. xi, 227 pp., illus.

HOOD   William C. Hood and Tjalling C. Koopmans (eds.), *Studies in Econometric Method*, Cowles Commission Monograph 14. New York: John Wiley & Sons, Inc., 1953. xix, 323 pp., illus.

KENDALL   Maurice G. Kendall, *The Advanced Theory of Statistics*, vols. I, II. London: Charles Griffin & Co., Ltd., 1943; 5th ed., 1952. Vol. I, xii, 457 pp., illus.; vol. II, vii, 521 pp. illus.

KLEIN   Lawrence R. Klein, *A Textbook of Econometrics*. Evanston: Row, Peterson & Company, 1953. ix, 355 pp., illus.

KOOPMANS   Tjalling C. Koopmans (ed.), *Statistical Inference in Dynamic Economic Models*, Cowles Commission Monograph 10. New York: John Wiley & Sons, Inc., 1950. xiv, 438 pp., illus.

TINBERGEN   Jan Tinbergen, *Econometrics*, translated from the Dutch by H. Rijken van Olst. New York: McGraw-Hill Book Company, Inc., Blakiston Division, 1951. xii, 258 pp., illus.

TINTNER   Gerhard Tintner, *Econometrics*. New York: John Wiley & Sons, Inc., 1952. xiii, 370 pp.

CHAPTER 1

The fundamental proposition
of econometrics

1.1. What econometrics is about

An econometrician's job is to express economic theories in mathematical terms in order to verify them by statistical methods, and to measure the impact of one economic variable on another so as to be able to predict future events or advise what economic policy should be followed when such and such a result is desired.

This definition describes the major divisions of econometrics, namely, specification, estimation, verification, and prediction.

Specification has to do with expressing an economic theory in mathematical terms. This activity is also called *model building*. A *model* is a set of mathematical relations (usually equations) expressing an economic theory. Successful model building requires an artist's touch, a sense of what to leave out if the set is to be kept manageable, elegant, and useful with the raw materials (collected data) that are available. This book deals only incidentally with the "specification" aspect of econometrics.

The problem of *estimation* is to use shrewdly our all too scanty data,

1

so as to fill the formal equations that make up the model with numerical values that are good and trustworthy.   Suppose we have the following simple theory to quantify: Consumption today (C) depends on yesterday's income (Z) in such a way that equal increments of income, no matter what income level you start from, always bring equal increments in consumption.   Letting α stand for consumption at zero income and γ for the marginal propensity to consume, this theory can be expressed thus:

$$C_t = \alpha + \gamma Z_t \tag{1-1}$$

The problem of estimation (and the main concern of this book) is to discover how to use whatever experience we have about consumption C and income Z in order to make a shrewd guess about how large α and γ might really be.   The problem of estimation is to guess correctly α and γ, the *parameters* (or inherent characteristics) of the consumption function.

Point estimation is making the *best possible single guess* about α and about γ.   *Interval estimation* is guessing how far our guess of α may be from the true α, and our guess of γ from the true γ.

It is not enough, of course, to be able to make correct point and interval estimates.   We want to make them as cheaply as possible. We are interested in *efficient programming of computations*, *checks of accuracy*, and *short cuts*.   Though this aspect of estimation will not occupy us very much, I shall give some computational advice from time to time.

Verification sets up criteria of success and uses these criteria to accept or reject the economic theory we are testing with the model and our data.   It is a tricky subject deeply rooted in the mathematical theory of statistics.

Prediction involves rearranging the model into convenient shape, so that we can feed it information about new developments in exogenous and lagged variables and grind out answers about the impact of these variables on the endogenous variables.

1.2. Mathematical tools

In explaining how to fashion good estimates for the parameters of an econometric model I shall often step into the mathematical statistician's toolroom to bring out one gadget or another required by the next step of our procedure. These digressions are clearly marked so they can be skipped by those acquainted with the tool in question.

The mathematical tools used again and again are elementary: *analytic geometry*, which makes equations and graphs interchangeable; *probability*, a concept enabling us to make precise statements about uncertain events; the *derivative* (or the operation of *differentiating*), which is a help in making a "best" guess among all possible guesses; *moments*, which are a sophisticated way of averaging various magnitudes; and *matrices*, which are nothing but many-dimensional ordinary numbers—indeed, statements that are true of ordinary numbers seldom fail for matrices—for instance, you can add, subtract, multiply, and divide matrices analogously to numbers and, in general, handle them as if they were ordinary numbers though perhaps more fragile; a *vector* is a special kind of matrix.

1.3. Outline of procedure and main discoveries in the next hundred pages

I. We shall deal first with models consisting of a *single* equation. We shall find that even in this simple case there are important difficulties.
  A. It is not always possible to estimate the parameters of even a single-equation model, for two sorts of reason:
    1. We may lack *enough* data. This is called the *problem of degrees of freedom*.
    2. Though the data are plentiful, they may not be *rich* or *varied* enough. This is the *problem of multicollinearity*.
  B. Our second important finding will be that "pedestrian" methods of estimation, for example the least squares fit, are apt to be treacherous. They either give us erroneous impressions about the true values of the parameters or waste the data.
II. Turning then to models containing two or more equations, our main findings will be the following:
  A. It is sometimes impossible to determine the value of each parameter in each equation, but this time not merely for lack of *data* or their monotony, but rather because the *equations* look too much like one another to be disentangled. Econ-

ometricians call this undesirable property *lack of identifiability*.

B. Nonpedestrian, statistically sophisticated methods become very complex and costly to compute when the model increases from a single equation even to two.

C. Happily, however, by sacrificing some of the rigor of these ideal "equestrian" methods in special, shrewd ways, we can cut the burden of computation by a factor of 5 or 10 and still get pretty good results. Such techniques are called *limited information techniques*, because they deliberately disregard refinements that should ideally be taken into account. Most theoretical econometricians work in this field, because the need is very great to know not only how to boil down complexity with clever tricks but also precisely how much each trick costs us in accuracy.

1.4. All-importance of statistical assumptions

The key word in estimation is the word *stochastic*. Its opposite is *exact* or *systematic*.

Stochastic comes from the Greek *stokhos* (a target, or bull's-eye). The outcome of throwing darts is a *stochastic* process, that is to say, fraught with occasional misses. In economics, indeed in all empirical disciplines, we do not expect our predictions to hit the bull's-eye 100 per cent of the time.

Econometrics begins by saying a great deal more about this matter of missing the mark. Where ordinary economic theory merely recognizes that we miss the mark now and then, econometrics makes *statistical assumptions*. These are precise statements about the particular way the darts hit the target's rim or hit the wall. Everything— estimation, prediction, and verification—depends vitally on the content of the statistical assumptions. Econometric models emphasize this fact by using a special variable u called the *error term*. The error term varies from instance to instance, just as one dart falls above, another below, one to the left, another to the right, of the target. A subscript t serves to indicate the various values of the error term. To make model (1-1) stochastic, we write

$$C_t = \alpha + \gamma Z_t + u_t \tag{1-2}$$

Before going on to rationalize the presence of the error term u in equation (1-2), two things must be explained. First, u could have been included as a multiplicative factor or as an exponential rather than as an additive term. Second, its subscript t need not express time. It can refer just as well to various countries or income classes.

To facilitate the exposition, I shall henceforth treat u_t as an additive term and take t to represent time. Exceptions will be clearly labeled. The common-sense interpretation of additivity is deferred to Sec. 1.11.

1.5. Rationalization of the error term

There are four types of reasons why an econometric model should be stochastic and not exact: incomplete theory, imperfect specification, aggregation of data, and errors of measurement. Not all of them apply to every model.

1. *Incomplete theory*

A theory is necessarily incomplete, an abstraction that cannot explain everything. For instance, in our simple theory of consumption,

a. We have left out possible variables, like wealth and liquid assets, that also affect consumption.

b. We have left out equations. The economy is much more complex than a single equation, no matter how many explanatory variables this single equation may contain; there may be other links between consumption and income besides the consumption function.[1]

c. Human behavior is "ultimately" random.

2. *Imperfect specification*

We have linearized a possibly nonlinear relationship.

3. *Aggregation of data*

We have aggregated over dissimilar individuals. Even if each of them possessed his own α and γ and if his consumption reacted in exact (nonstochastic) fashion to his past income, total consumption would not be likely to react exactly in response to a given total income, because its distribution may change. Another way of putting this is:

---

[1] How many independent links there may be and how we are to find them is itself a problem in statistical inference, and is treated briefly in Chap. 10.

Variables expressing individual peculiarities are missing (cf. 1a). Or this way: Equations that describe income distribution are missing (cf. 1b).

4. *Errors of measurement*

Even if behavior were exact, survey methods are not, and our statistical series for consumption and income contain some errors of measurement. Throughout this book we pretend that all variables are measured without error.

1.6. The fundamental proposition

All we get out of an econometric model is already implied in:

1. *Its specification;* that is to say, consumption C depends on yesterday's income Z as in the equation $C_t = \alpha + \gamma Z_t + u_t$ and in no other way[1]

2. *Our assumptions concerning u,* that is to say, the particular way we suppose the relationship between C and Z to be inexact[2]

3. *Our sampling procedure,* namely, the way we arrange to get data

4. *Our sample,* i.e., the *particular* data that happen to turn up *after* we *decide* how to look for them

5. *Our estimating criterion,* i.e., what properties we desire our estimates of α and γ to have, short of the unattainable: absolute correctness

Over items 1, 2, 3, and 5 we have absolute control; for we are free to change our theory of consumption, our set of assumptions concerning the error term, our data-collecting techniques, and our estimating criterion. We have no control over item 4; for what data actually turn up is a matter of luck.

According to this fundamental proposition, what estimates we get for the parameters (α and γ) depends, among other things, on the *stochastic assumptions,* i.e., what we choose to suppose about the behavior of the error term u. Every set of assumptions about the error term prescribes a certain way of guessing at the true value of the parameters. And conversely, every guess about the parameters is implicitly a set of stochastic assumptions.

---

[1] This is also called "structural specification."
[2] This is also called "stochastic specification."

The relationship between stochastic assumptions and parameter estimates is not always a one-to-one relationship. A given set of stochastic assumptions is compatible with several sets of different parameter estimates, and conversely. In practice, we don't have to worry about these possibilities, because we shall be making assumptions about u that lead to unique guesses about α and γ, or, at the very worst, to a few different guesses. Also, in practice, since we usually are interested in α and γ, not in verifying our assumptions about u, it does not matter that many different u assumptions are compatible with a single set of parameter estimates.

1.7. Population and sample

The whole of statistics rests on the distinction between *population* and *observation* or *sample*. People were receiving income and consuming it long before econometrics and statistics were dreamed of. There is, so to speak, an underlying population of C's and Z's, which we can enumerate, hypothetically, as follows:

$$C_1, C_2, \ldots, C_p, \ldots, C_P \quad \text{or} \quad C_p \text{ for } p = 1, 2, \ldots, P$$
$$Z_1, Z_2, \ldots, Z_p, \ldots, Z_P \quad \text{or} \quad Z_p \text{ for } p = 1, 2, \ldots, P$$

Of these C's and Z's we may have observed all or some. Those that we have observed take on a different index s instead of p, to emphasize that they form a subset of the population. All we observe, then, is C_s and Z_s, where the s assumes some (perhaps all) of the values that p runs, but no more. Index s can start running anywhere, say, at $p = 5$, assume the values 6 and 7, skip 8, 25, and 92, and stop anywhere short of the value P or at P itself. In all cases that I shall discuss, the sample covers *consecutive* time periods, which are renumbered, for convenience, in such a way that the beginning of time coincides with the beginning of the sample, not of the population. Whether the sample is consecutive or not sometimes does and sometimes does not affect the estimation of α and γ.

Note that we mean by the term *sample* a given *collection* of observations, like $\mathbf{S} = (C_9, C_{10}, C_{11}; Z_9, Z_{10}, Z_{11})$, not an isolated observation. $\mathbf{S}$ is *a* sample of *three* observations, the following ones: (C_9, Z_9), (C_{10}, Z_{10}), and (C_{11}, Z_{11}). Samples made up of a single observation can exist, of course, but we seldom work with so little observation.

1.8. Parameters and estimates

Another crucial distinction is between a *parameter* and its *estimate*. If the theory is correct, there are, hiding somewhere, the true α and γ. These we never observe. What we do do is *guess* at them, basing ourselves on such evidence and common sense as we may have. The guesses, or estimates, always wear a badge to distinguish them from the parameters themselves.

CONVENTION

We shall use three kinds of badge for a parameter estimate: a roof-shaped *hat*, as in $\hat{\alpha}$, $\hat{\gamma}$, to mark *maximum likelihood* estimates; a *bird*, the same symbol upside down, as in $\check{\alpha}$, $\check{\gamma}$, for *naïve least squares* estimates; and the *wiggle*, as in $\tilde{\alpha}$, $\tilde{\gamma}$, for *other* kinds of estimates or for estimates whose kind we do not wish to specify. These types of estimate are defined in Chap. 2.

The distinction between *error* and *residual* is analogous to the distinction between parameter and estimate. The *error* u_t is *never observed*, although we may speculate about its behavior. It always goes with the real α and γ, as in (1-2), whereas the *residual*, which is an estimate of the error and whose symbol always wears a distinctive badge, *can be calculated*, provided we have settled on a particular guess $(\hat{\alpha}, \hat{\gamma})$ or $(\tilde{\alpha}, \tilde{\gamma})$ for the parameters. The value of the error does not depend on our guessing; it is just there, in the population and, therefore, in the sample. The residual, however, depends on the particular guess. To emphasize this fact we put the same badge on the residual as on the corresponding parameter estimate. We write, for example, $C_t = \hat{\alpha} + \hat{\gamma} Z_t + \hat{u}_t$ or $C_t = \tilde{\alpha} + \tilde{\gamma} Z_t + \tilde{u}_t$.

Now we can state precisely what the problem of estimation is, as follows. We assume a theory, for example, the theory of consumption $C_t = \alpha + \gamma Z_t + u_t$; we assume that u_t behaves in some particular way (to which the next section is devoted); we get a set of observations on C and Z (the sample). Then we manipulate the sample data to give us estimates $\tilde{\alpha}$ and $\tilde{\gamma}$ that satisfy our estimating criterion (discussed in Chap. 2). Then we compute if we wish the residuals $\tilde{u}_t$ as estimates of the errors u_t.

1.9. Assumptions about the error term

Besides additivity (Sec. 1.4) we shall now make and interpret six assumptions about the error term.   Of these, the first is indispensable, exactly as it stands.   The other five could be different in content or in number.   Note carefully that these are statements about the u's not the $\bar{u}$'s.

Assumption 1.   *u is a random real variable.*

If the model is stochastic, either its systematic variables (consumption or income) are measured with errors, or the consumption function itself is subject to random disturbances, or both.   Since we have ruled out (Sec. 1.5) errors of measurement, the relationship itself has to be stochastic.

"Random" is one of those words whose meaning everybody knows but few can define.   Unpardonably, few standard texts give its definition.   A *variable* is *random* if it takes on a number of different values, each with a certain probability.   Its different values can be infinite in number and can range all over the field, provided there are at least two of them.   For instance, a variable w that is equal to $-\frac{1}{2}$ twenty-five per cent of the time, to $3 + \sqrt{2}$ forty per cent of the time, and to $+35.3$ thirty-five per cent of the time is a random variable. We may or may not know what values it takes on or their probabilities.   Its probability distribution may or may not be expressible analytically.   (See Sec. 2.2.)

Digression on the distinction between probability and probability density

A random variable w can be *discrete*, like the number of remaining teeth in members of a group of people, or *continuous*, like their weight.   If w takes on a finite number of values, their probabilities can be quite simply plotted on and read off a *dot diagram* or *point graph* (Fig. 1a).

With a continuous variable we can usually speak only of the probability that its value should lie between (or at) such and such limits.   In this case, we plot a *probability-density graph*

(Fig. 1b).   The height of such a graph *at a point* is the *probability density*, and the relative area under the graph between any two points of the w axis is the *probability*.

Assumption 2. u_t, *for every* t, *has zero expected value.*

Naïvely interpreted, this proposition says that the "average" value of u_1 is zero, that of u_2 is also zero, and so forth.   Or, to put it differently, it says that a prediction like $C_1 = \alpha + \gamma Z_1$ is "on the average" correct, that the same is true of $C_2 = \alpha + \gamma Z_2$, and so forth.

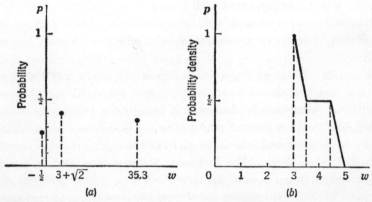

Fig. 1. A random variable.   *a.* Variable w is discrete.   The illustration is a *dot diagram*, or *point graph*.   *b.* Variable w is continuous.   The illustration is a *probability-density graph*.

The trouble begins when you begin to wonder what "on the average" can possibly mean if you stick to a single instance, like time period 1 (or time period 2).   For every event happens in a particular way and not otherwise.   Suppose, for instance, that in the year 1776 ($t = 1776$) consumption fell short of its theoretical level $\alpha + \gamma Z_{1776}$ by 2.24 million dollars, that is, that $u_{1776} = -2.24$.   Obviously, then, the average value of u_{1776} is exactly -2.24.   What could we possibly wish to convey by the statement that u_{1776} (and every other u_t) has zero expected value?

One should never identify the concept of expected value with the concept of the arithmetic mean.   *Arithmetic mean* denotes the sum of a set of N numbers divided by N and is an algebraic concept.   *Expected value* is a statistical or combinatorial concept.   You have to imagine an urn containing a (finite or infinite) number of balls, each with a number written on it.   Consider now all the possible ways one could draw *one* ball from such an urn.   The arithmetic mean of the numbers that would turn up if we exhausted all possible ways of drawing one ball is the expected value.

The random term of an econometric model is assumed to come from an Urn of Nature which, at every moment of time, contains balls with numbers that add up to zero.

The common-sense interpretation of Nature's Urn is as follows: Though in 1776 actual consumption in fact fell short of the theoretical by 2.24 and no other amount, the many causes that interacted to produce $u_{1776} = -2.24$ *could have* interacted (in 1776) in various other ways.   This, theoretically, they were free to do since they were random causes.   Now, try to think of all conceivable combinations of these causes—or if you prefer, think of very many 1776 worlds, identical in all respects except in the combinations of random causes that generated the random term.   Let us have as many such worlds as there are theoretical combinations of the causes behind the random term.   In some worlds the causes act overwhelmingly to make consumption lower than the nonstochastic level $\alpha + \gamma Z_{1776}$; in other worlds the causes act so as to make it greater than $\alpha + \gamma Z_{1776}$; and in a few worlds the causes cancel out, so that $C_{1776} = \alpha + \gamma Z_{1776}$ exactly. Now consider the random terms of all possible worlds, and (says the assumption) they will average out to zero.

This interpretation is a conceptual model we can never hope to prove or disprove.   Its chief merit is that it reduces chance and statistics to the (relatively) easy language and theorems of combinatorial algebra.   Some people take it seriously; others (myself included) use it for lack of anything better.

Digression on the distinction between "population" and "universe"

Whether or not we take Nature's Urn seriously, we will be well advised to acknowledge that we are dealing with three levels of discourse, not just the two that I called *population* and *sample*. The third and deeper level is called the *universe*.   It contains all events as they have happened and as they *might have* happened if everything else had remained the same but the random shocks.

Level I   Sample: things that both happened and were observed. It is drawn from

Level II   Population: things that happened but were not necessarily observed.   It is drawn from

Level III   Universe: all things that could have happened.   (In the nature of things only a few did.)

CONVENTION

We shall henceforth use four types of running subscript:

$$s = 1, 2, \ldots, S \qquad \text{for the sample}$$
$$p = 1, 2, \ldots, P \qquad \text{for the population}$$
$$i = 1, 2, \ldots, I \qquad \text{for the universe}$$
$$t = 1, 2, \ldots, T \qquad \text{for instances in general, whether they come from the sample, the population, or the universe}$$

In a sense the population (C_p, Z_p) of consumption and income as they *actually* happened in recorded and unrecorded history is merely a sample from the universe (C_i, Z_i) of all possible worlds. Naturally, what we call the sample is drawn from the population of actual events, not from the hypothetical universe of level III. In most instances it does no harm to speak (and prove theorems) as if level I were picked directly from level III, not from level II.

The Platonic universe of level III is indeed rather unseemly for the field of statistics (which is surely, in lay opinion, the most hard-boiled of mathematics, resting solidly on "facts") and has been amusingly ridiculed by Hogben.[1]

The next few paragraphs state why the abstract model of Nature's Urn is a less appropriate foundation for econometrics than for statistical physics or biology.   But the rest of the book goes merrily on using the said Urn.

Economic and physical phenomena alike take place in time.

---

[1] Lancelot Hogben, F. R. S., *Statistical Theory: The Relationship of Probability, Credibility, and Error; An Examination of the Contemporary Crisis in Statistical Theory from a Behaviourist Viewpoint*, pp. 98–105 (London: George Allen & Unwin Ltd., 1957).

In both fields, the statement that u_t is a random variable for *each*
t is inevitably an abstraction, because time runs on inexorably.
In the physical sciences events are deemed "repeatable," or arising from a universe "fixed in repeated samples," primarily
because the experimenter can *ideally* replicate exactly all systematically significant conditions that had surrounded his original
event.   This is not possible in social phenomena of the "irreversible" or "progressive" type.   Although in the physical
sciences it may be safe to neglect the difference between population and universe, it is unsafe in econometrics.   For, as economic
phenomena take place in time, all other conditions, including
the exogenous variables, move on to new levels, often never to
return.   The common-sense phrase "on the average over similar
experiments" makes much more sense in a laboratory science
than in economics.

Nature's Urn also supports *maximum likelihood, variance of an
estimate, bias, consistency*, and many other notions we shall have
occasion to introduce in later chapters.   All these rest on the
notion of "all conceivable samples."   The class of *all conceivable
samples* includes first of all samples of all conceivable sizes; it also
includes all conceivable samples of a given size, say, 4.   A sample
of size 4 may consist of *points* that actually happened (if so, they
are in the population); it also could consist (partly or entirely)
of points in the universe but not in the population.   The latter
kind of sample is easy to conceive but impossible to draw, because
the imagined points never "happened."   Therefore, even a complete census of what happened is not enough for constructing an
exhaustive list of all conceivable samples.

Assumption 3.   The variance of u_t is constant over time.

This means merely that, in each year, u_t is drawn from an identical
Urn, or universe.   This assumption states that the causes underlying
the random term remain unchanged in number, relative importance,
and absolute impact, although, in any particular year, one or another
of them may fail to operate.

For simplicity's sake we have assumed no errors of measurement.
In fact there may be some, and their typical size could vary systematically with time (or with the independent variable Z).   If we try

to measure the diameter of a distant star, our error of measurement is likely to be several million miles; when we measure the diameter of Sputnik, it can be only a few feet. Likewise, if our data stretch from 1850 to 1950, national income increases by a factor of 20. It is quite likely that errors of measurement, too, should increase absolutely. If they do, Assumption 3 is violated, and some of the techniques that I develop below should not be used.

Digression on infinite variances

The variance of u is not only constant but finite. When u is normal it is unnecessary to stipulate that its variance is finite, because *all* nondegenerate normal distributions have finite variance. There exist, however, nondegenerate distributions with zero mean and infinite variance, for example, the discrete random variable

$$\ldots, \quad -16, \quad -8, \quad -4, \quad 4, \quad 8, \quad 16, \quad \ldots$$

with probabilities, respectively,

$$\ldots, \quad \tfrac{1}{16}, \quad \tfrac{1}{8}, \quad \tfrac{1}{4}, \quad \tfrac{1}{4}, \quad \tfrac{1}{8}, \quad \tfrac{1}{16}, \quad \ldots$$

The central limit theorem, according to which the sum of N random variables (distributed in any form) approaches the normal distribution for large N, is valid only if the original distributions have finite variances.

Assumption 4. *The error term is normally distributed.*

This is a rather strong restriction. We impose it mainly because normal distributions are easy to work with.

Digression on the univariate normal distribution

The single-variable normal distribution is shaped like a symmetrical two-dimensional bell whose mouth is wider than the mouth of anything you might name. Normal distributions come tall, medium, and squat (i.e., with small, medium, or large variances). And the top of the bell can be over any point of the

w axis; that is to say, the mean of the normal can be negative, zero, or positive, large or small.   This distribution's chief characteristic is that extreme values are more and more unlikely the more extreme they get.

For instance, the likelihood that all the people christened John and living in London will die today is extremely small, and the likelihood that none of them will die today is equally small. Now why is this?   Because London is not under atomic attack, the Johns are not all aboard a single bus, not all of them are diving from the London Bridge, nor were they all born 85 years ago. Each goes about his business more or less independently of the others (except, perhaps, father-and-son teams of Johns), some old, some young, some exposing themselves to danger and others not. The reason why the probability that w of these Johns will die today approximates the normal is that there are very many of them and that each is subjected to a vast number of independent influences, like age, food, heredity, job, and so forth.   This probability would not be normal if the Johns were really few, if the causes working toward their deaths were few, or if such causes were many but linked with one another.

The assumption that u is normal is justified if we can show that the variables left out of equation (1-2) are infinitely numerous and not interlinked.   If they are *merely* very many and not interlinked, then u is *approximately* normal.   If they are infinitely many but enough of them are interlinked, then u is not even approximately normal. We often know or suspect that these variables, such as wealth, liquid balances, age, residence, and so forth, are quite interlinked and are very likely to be present together or absent together.

Sometimes the following argument is advanced: In our model of consumption, the error term u stems from many sources; that is, we have left out variables, we have left out equations, we have linearized, we have aggregated, and so on.   These are all different operations, presumably not linked with one another.   Therefore, u is normally distributed.

This argument is, of course, a bad heuristic argument, and it does not even stand for an existing (but difficult) rigorous argument.   It is logically untidy to count as arguments for the normality of u, on one and the same level of discourse, such diverse items as the fact of linearization and the number of unspecified variables that affect consumption.

The assumption stands or falls on the argument of many non-interlinked absent variables. Most alternative assumptions cause great computational grief.

Assumption 5.   The random terms of different time periods are independent.

This assumption requires that in each period the causes that determine the random term act independently of their behavior in all previous and subsequent periods.   It is easy to violate this assumption.

1. The error term includes variables that act cyclically. If, for example, we think consumption has a bulge every 3 years because that is how often we get substantially remodeled cars, this effect should be introduced as a separate variable and not included in u.

2. The model is subject to cobweb phenomena. Suppose that consumers in year 1 (for any reason) underestimate their income, so that they consume less than the theoretical amount. Then in year 2 they discover the error and make it up by consuming more than the theoretical amount of year 2; and so on.

3. One of the causes behind the random term may be an employee's vacation, which is usually in force for 2 weeks though the model's unit period is 1 week. Any such behavior violates the requirement that the error of any period be independent of the error in all previous periods.

Assumption 6.   The error is not correlated with any predetermined variable.

To appreciate this assumption, suppose that (for whatever reason) sellers set today's price p_t on the basis of the change in the quantity sold yesterday over the day before; that is,

$$p_t = \alpha + \gamma(q_{t-1} - q_{t-2}) + u_t$$

Suppose, further, that the greater (and more evident) the change in q

the more they strive to set a price according to the above rule.   Such
behavior violates Assumption 6.

We can think of examples where behavior is fairly exact (small u's)
for moderate values of the independent variable, but quite erratic for
very large or very small values of the independent variable.   I am
apt, for instance, to stumble more if there is either too little or too
much light in the room.   This, again, violates Assumption 6, because
the error in the stochastic equation describing my motion depends on
the intensity of light.

So we come to the end of our statistical assumptions about the error
u.   When in future discussion I speak of u as having "all the Simplify-
ing Properties" (or as "satisfying all the Simplifying Assumptions"),
I mean exactly these six.

Certain of these six assumptions can be checked or statistically
verified from a sample; others cannot.   I shall return to this topic
later.

Of these assumptions only Assumption 1 is obligatory.   There are
decent estimating procedures for other sets of assumptions.

1.10. Mathematical restatement of the Six Simplifying Assumptions

1. u_t is random for every t: Some $p(u)$ is defined for all u, such
that

$$0 \leq p \leq 1 \quad \text{and} \quad \int_u p(u) \, du = 1$$

2. The expected value of u_t is zero:

$$\varepsilon u_t = 0 \quad \text{for all } t$$

3. The variance $\sigma_{uu}(t)$ is constant in time, and finite:

$$0 < \sigma_{uu}(t) = \text{cov} \, (u_t, u_t) = \sigma_{uu} < \infty \quad \text{for all } t$$

4. u_t is normal:

$$p(u) = (2\pi)^{-\frac{1}{2}} \det (\sigma_{uu})^{-\frac{1}{2}} \exp \left[-\tfrac{1}{2}(u - \varepsilon u)(\sigma_{uu})^{-1}(u - \varepsilon u) \right]$$

I explain this fancy notation in the next chapter.   I use it because it generalizes very handily into many dimensions. The usual way to write the normal distribution is

$$p(u) = \frac{1}{\sigma \sqrt{2\pi}} \exp\left[-\frac{1}{2} \left(\frac{u - \varepsilon u}{\sigma} \right)^2 \right]$$

The symbol σ_{uu} is the square of σ; σ_{uu} is the variance of u.

5. u is not autocorrelated:

$$\varepsilon(u_t, u_{t-\theta}) = 0 \qquad \text{for all } t \text{ and for } \theta \neq 0$$

6. u is fully independent of the variable Z:

$$\text{cov}\ (u_t, Z_{t-\theta}) = 0 \qquad \text{for all } t \text{ and all } \theta$$

1.11. Interpretation of additivity

The random term u appears in model (1-2) as an *additive* term. This fact rules out interaction effects between u and Z. Absence of interaction effects means that, no matter what the level of income Z may be, a random term of a given magnitude always has the same effect on consumption. Its impact does not depend on the level of income.

1.12. Recapitulation

We must be very clear in econometrics, as well as in other areas of statistical inference, about what is assumed, what is observed, and what is guessed, and also about what criterion the guess should satisfy. Table 1.1 provides a check list of things we accept by assumption, things we can and cannot do, and things we must do in making statistical estimates. The items in the first three columns have been introduced in this chapter; the estimating criteria in the fourth column will be discussed in the next chapter.

Digression on the differences among moment, expectation, and covariance

Consider two variables, consumption c and yesterday's income z. They may or may not be functionally related. They have a

Table 1.1

THESE THINGS ARE ASSUMED	THESE THINGS ARE OBSERVED	THESE THINGS ARE NOT OBSERVED	THIS IS IMPOSED	THESE THINGS ARE COMPUTED BY US
That a true α and a true γ exist		The true α and γ	Some estimating criterion for computing $\bar{\alpha}, \bar{\gamma}, \tilde{u}$	$\bar{\alpha}$, a guess as to α $\bar{\gamma}$, a guess as to γ
That a true u_t exists in each time period		The true u_t		The residuals $\tilde{u}_s$ $(s = 1, 2, \ldots, S)$
That u_t has the Six Simplifying Properties		εu, the expected value σ_{uu}, the variance of the error		$(\Sigma \tilde{u}_s)/S$, the mean of the residuals $\tilde{u}_s$ $m_{\tilde{u}\tilde{u}}$, the moment of the residuals $\tilde{u}_s$
That there is a universe C_i, Z_i $(i = 1, 2, \ldots, I)$ in which $C_i = \alpha + \gamma Z_i + u_i$	The C's and Z's of the sample denoted by C_s, Z_s $(s = 1, 2, \ldots, S)$	The C's and Z's not in the sample		

universe

$$\mathbf{U} = \begin{bmatrix} c_1, & \cdots, & c_i, & \cdots, & c_I \\ z_1, & \cdots, & z_i, & \cdots, & z_I \end{bmatrix}$$

Expectation

The average value of *c in the universe* is symbolized by εc (read "expected value of *c*" or "expectation of *c*"). Similarly, εz is the average *z in the universe*.

Covariance

The *covariance of c and z* is defined as the expected value

$$\mathrm{E}(c_i - \varepsilon c)(z_i - \varepsilon z)$$

where *i* runs *over the entire universe*. This is symbolized by cov (c, z) or σ_{cz}.

Variance

The *variance of c* is simply the covariance of *c* and *c*. It is written var *c*, or cov (c, c), or σ_{cc}.

Now consider a specific sample S^0 made up of specific (corresponding) pairs of consumption and income, for instance,

$$S^0 = \begin{bmatrix} c_{27}, & c_{54}, & c_{105} \\ z_{27}, & z_{54}, & z_{105} \end{bmatrix}$$

Let the sample means for this particular sample be written c^0 and z^0, respectively.

Moment

The *moment* (*for sample* S^0) *of c on z* is defined as the expected value

$$E(c_s - c^0)(z_s - z^0)$$

where s runs over 27, 54, and 105 only. It is symbolized by $m_{c \cdot z}(S^0)$ or $m_{c \cdot z}$ or simply m_{cz}. Of course, a different sample S^1 would give a different moment $m_{c \cdot z}(S^1)$.

Expectation of a moment

Now consider all samples of size 3 that we can draw (with replacement) from the universe U. Then the *expectation of* m_{cz} is the average of the various moments $m_{c \cdot z}(S^0)$, $m_{c \cdot z}(S^1)$, etc., when *all* conceivable samples of size 3 are taken into account. A universe with I elements generates $\binom{I}{3}$ such samples, and the means $\bar{c}$ and $\bar{z}$ of the two variables vary from sample to sample.

The expectation of m_{cz} for samples *of size* 4 is, in general, a different value altogether.

Much confusion will be avoided later on if these distinctions are kept in mind. Clear up any questions by doing the exercises below.

Exercises

1.A If c, c', c'', c^* are four independent drawings (with replacement) from the universe U, prove that $\varepsilon(c' + c'' + c^*) = 3 \, \varepsilon c$.

1.B If c, z, q are variables and k is a constant, which of the following relations are identities?

$$\text{cov } (c,z) = \text{cov } (z,c)$$
$$m_{cz} = m_{zc}$$
$$\varepsilon(c + z) = \varepsilon c + \varepsilon z$$
$$\text{cov } (kc,z) = k \text{ cov } (c,z)$$
$$\text{var } (kq) = k^2 \text{ var } q$$
$$m_{(kc) \cdot z} = km_{cz}$$
$$\text{cov } (c + q,z) = \text{cov } (c, z) + \text{cov } (q,z)$$

Further readings

The art of model specification is learned by practice and by studying cleverly contrived models. BEACH,[1] KLEIN, TINBERGEN, and TINTNER give several examples. L. R. Klein and A. S. Goldberger, *An Econometric Model of the United States: 1929–1952* (Amsterdam: North-Holland Publishing Company, 1957), present a celebrated large-scale econometric model. Chapters 1 and 2 give a good idea of the difficulties of estimation. The performance of this model is appraised by Karl A. Fox in "Econometric Models of the United States" (*Journal of Political Economy*, vol. 44, no. 2, pp. 128–142, April, 1956) and by Carl Christ in "Aggregate Econometric Models" (*American Economic Review*, vol. 46, no. 3, pp. 385–408, June, 1956).

"The Dynamics of the Onion Market," by Daniel B. Suits and Susumu Koizumi (*Journal of Farm Economics*, vol. 38, no. 2, pp. 475–484, May, 1956), is an interesting example of econometrics applied to a particular market in the short run.

KENDALL, chap. 7, reviews the logic of probability, sampling, and expected value. For a lucid discussion of the concept of randomness, see M. G. Kendall, "A Theory of Randomness" (*Biometrika*, vol. 32, pt. 1, pp. 1–15, January, 1941).

As far as I know, the assumptions about the random term have not been discussed systematically from the economic point of view, except for Marschak's brief passage (pp. 12–15) in HOOD, chap. 1, sec. 7. See also Gerhard Tintner, *The Variate Difference Method* (Cowles Commission Monograph 5, pp. 4–5 and appendixes VI, VII, Bloomington, Indiana: Principia Press, 1940), and Tintner, "A Note on Economic Aspects of the Theory of Errors in Time Series" (*Quarterly Journal of Economics*, vol. 53, no. 1, pp. 141–149, November, 1938).

As defined in economics textbooks, the production function and the cost function necessarily violate Assumption 2. In no instance (whether in the universe, the population, or the sample) can the random disturbance exceed zero in the production function and fall short of zero in the average cost

[1] See Frequent References at front of book. Works of authors whose names are capitalized are listed there.

function. All statistical studies of production and cost functions I know of have implicitly used the assumption that $\varepsilon u = 0$. The error is in the assumption of normality. See, for instance, Joel Dean, "Department Store Cost Functions," in *Studies in Mathematical Economics and Econometrics*, in memory of Henry Schultz, edited by Oscar Lange, Francis McIntyre, and Theodore O. Yntema (p. 222, Chicago: University of Chicago Press, 1942), which is also an interesting attempt to fit static cost functions to data from years of large dynamic changes. In this respect I was guilty myself in "An Econometric Model of Growth: U.S.A. 1869–1953" (*American Economic Review*, vol. 45, no. 2, pp. 208–221, May, 1955).

For examples of nonadditive disturbances, see Hurwicz, "Systems with Nonadditive Disturbances," chap. 18 of KOOPMANS, pp. 410–418.

CHAPTER 2

Estimating criteria and the method
of least squares

2.1. Outline of the chapter

This chapter, like the previous one, deals exclusively with single-equation models. Unless the contrary is stated, all the Simplifying Assumptions of Sec. 1.9 remain in force. The main points of this chapter are the following:

1. Once we have specified the model and made certain stochastic assumptions, our sample tells us nothing about the unknown parameters of the model unless we adopt an *estimating criterion*.

2. A very reasonable (and hard to replace) criterion is *maximum likelihood*. It is based on the assumption that, while we were taking the sample, Nature performed for our benefit the most likely thing, or generated for us her most probable sample.

3. Once the maximum likelihood criterion is adopted, we can tell precisely what the unknown parameters must be if our sample was the most likely to turn up. This is what is called *maximizing the likelihood function*. We find the unknowns by manipulating this function.

23

4. The familiar least squares fit arises as a special case of the operation of maximizing the likelihood function.

5. In many cases, adopting the maximum likelihood criterion automatically generates estimates that conform to other estimating criteria, for example *unbiasedness, consistency, efficiency.*

6. If estimates of the unknown parameters are unbiased, consistent, etc., this does not mean that our particular sample or method has given us a correct estimate. It means that, if we had infinite facilities (or infinite patience), we could get a correct estimate "in the long run" or "on the average."

7. The likelihood function not only tells us what values of the parameters give the greatest probability to the observed event but also attaches to such values degrees of credence, or reliability.

Though these statements can be made about all sorts of models, the single-equation model of consumption that I have been using all along captures the spirit of the procedure. Multi-equation models have all the complications of single-equation models plus many others.

2.2. Probability and likelihood

In common speech, *probability* and *likelihood* are but Latin and Saxon doublets. In statistics the two terms, though often interchanged for the sake of variety or style, have distinct meanings. *Probability* is a property of the sample; *likelihood* is a property of the unknown parameter values.

Probability

Imagine that, in a model that described Nature's workings perfectly, the true values of the parameters α, β, γ, . . . were such and such and that the true stochastic properties of the error term u were such and such. We would then say that certain types of natural behavior (i.e., certain samples or observations) were more probable than others. For example, if you knew that a river flowed gently southward at a speed of 3 miles per hour, that an engineless boat drifting on it had such and such dimensions, weight, and friction (the model); if, in addition, you knew that gentle breezes usually blow in the area, very rarely faster than 5 miles per hour, and that they usually blow now in one, now in another direction (the stochastic properties); then you would be very much surprised to find an instance in which the boat had traveled 25 miles northward or 30 miles southward in the space of 2 hours (the improbable behavior).

Likelihood

Now reverse the position. If you were sure of your information about the wind, if you did not know which way or how fast the river flowed, but you observed the boat 28 miles south of where it was 2 hours ago and were willing to assume that Nature took the most probable action while you happened to be observing her, then you would infer that the river must have a southward current of 14 miles per hour. This is the *maximum likelihood estimate*, or *most likely* (NOT most probable) speed of the river on the evidence of this unfortunate sample. Any other southward speed and any kind of northward flow are highly *unlikely*, or less *likely* than 14 miles per hour south.

To say that any other speed is less *probable* is to misuse the term. The river's speed is what it is (3 miles per hour to the south) and it cannot be more or less probable. What can be more or less probable is the particular observation: that the boat has traveled southward 28 miles. This observation is very improbable if the river indeed flows 3 miles per hour southward. It would be more probable if the river flowed southward with a speed of 5, 7, or 10 miles. And it would be most probable if the true speed of the river had been 14 miles per hour. Evidently, a maximum likelihood guess can be very far from the truth.

All estimation in econometrics operates as in this river example, no matter how elaborate the model, sloppy or exquisite the sample.

What is so commendable about the maximum likelihood criterion, if it cannot guarantee us correct or even nearly correct results? Why assume that Nature will do the most likely thing? All I can say to this is to ask: Well, what *shall* we assume instead? the *second* most likely thing? the *seventy-first?*

It is true that (in some cases) maximum likelihood estimates tend to be correct estimates "on the average" or "in the long run" (see Secs. 2.1 and 2.10). These facts, however, are irrelevant, because we use the maximum likelihood criterion even when we plan neither to repeat the experiment nor to enlarge the sample.

It is very important to appreciate just what maximum likelihood estimation does: The experimenter makes one observation, say, that the boat had traveled 28 miles southward in 2 hours; he then *asserts hopefully* (he *does not know* this) that the wind has been calm, because this is the most typical total net wind speed for all conceivable 2-hour stretches; and so he lets his estimate of the speed be 14 miles.

Actually, we (who happen to know that the true speed is 3 miles) realize that, while the experimenter was busy measuring, the weather was not at all typical but happened to be the improbable case of 2 hours of strong southerly wind.

The same experimenter under different circumstances might estimate the speed to be 6, 0.5, -2, -3.0, etc., miles per hour depending on the wind's actual whim during the 2-hour interval in which observation took place.

Exercise

2.A Set up an econometric model of the river-and-boat example of Sec. 2.2, using the following symbols: d_t for the number of miles (from a fixed point) traveled southward in t hours by the boat, γ for the (unknown) speed of the river in miles per hour, and u_t for the net southbound component of the wind's speed in miles per hour. Let u_t have the following stochastic specification:

10 per cent of the time	$u_t = 11$	(southbound)
70 per cent of the time	$u_t = 0$	(calm)
10 per cent of the time	$u_t = -5$	(northbound)
10 per cent of the time	$u_t = -6$	(northbound)

Construct a probability table giving the net wind effects *for 2 hours in succession*. For *each* type of conceivable observation, derive the maximum likelihood estimate of γ.

Digression on the multivariate normal distribution

The univariate normal distribution for a variable u with universe mean εu and variance σ_{uu} was written in Sec. 1.10 in the fancy form

$$p(u) = (2\pi)^{-N/2} \det (\sigma_{uu})^{-\frac{1}{2}} \exp \left[-\tfrac{1}{2}(u - \varepsilon u)(\sigma_{uu})^{-1}(u - \varepsilon u) \right]$$
$$(2\text{-}1)$$

because of the ease with which it generalizes to the multivariate case.

Let $u_1, u_2, \ldots, u_N$ be N variables which have a joint normal distribution. Define

$$\mathbf{u} = \text{vec } (u_1, u_2, \ldots, u_N)$$
$$\varepsilon\mathbf{u} = \text{vec } (\varepsilon u_1, \varepsilon u_2, \ldots, \varepsilon u_N)$$

$$\sigma_{\mathbf{uu}} = \begin{bmatrix} \sigma_{u_1 u_1} & \cdots & \sigma_{u_1 u_N} \\ \cdot & & \cdot \\ \cdot & & \cdot \\ \cdot & & \cdot \\ \sigma_{u_N u_1} & \cdots & \sigma_{u_N u_N} \end{bmatrix}$$

For $\sigma_{u_1 u_2}$ we often write cov (u_1, u_2), or simply σ_{12} if the meaning is clear from the context. Sometimes the inverse of $\sigma_{\mathbf{uu}}$, usually written $(\sigma_{\mathbf{uu}})^{-1}$, is written $\sigma^{\mathbf{uu}}$, and its elements are written $\sigma^{u_i u_j}$ or just σ^{ij}. These superscripts are *not* exponents. If we need to write an exponent we write it outside parentheses, as in equation (2-1).

To get the multivariate distribution for $u_1, u_2, \ldots, u_N$, all we need to do is change the italic u's of (2-1) into bold characters:

$$p(\mathbf{u}) = (2\pi)^{-N/2} \det (\sigma_{\mathbf{uu}})^{-\frac{1}{2}} \exp \left[-\tfrac{1}{2}(\mathbf{u} - \varepsilon\mathbf{u})(\sigma_{\mathbf{uu}})^{-1}(\mathbf{u} - \varepsilon\mathbf{u}) \right]$$
$$(2\text{-}2)$$

This illustrates the principle noted in Sec. 1.2: that if an operation, theorem, property, etc., holds for simple numbers, it holds analogously for matrices. This is a great convenience, because you can pretend that matrices are numbers and so collapse a complicated formula into a shorter and more intuitive expression. Moreover, by pretending a matrix is a number, you can get a clear impression of what a formula conveys.

Exercises

2.B Write explicitly the joint normal distribution of the two variables x and w.

2.C In Exercise 2.B, modify the formula for $\sigma_{xx} = \sigma_{ww}$ and $\sigma_{wx} = 0$.

2.D   Write in vector and matrix notation the formula

$$-\tfrac{1}{2} \sum_{m=1}^{N} \sum_{n=1}^{N} (w_m - \varepsilon w_m)\sigma^{mn}(w_n - \varepsilon w_n)$$

2.3. The concept of likelihood function

Consider again the river-and-boat illustration of the previous section.   Our information can come in one of several different ways.

1. *A sample of one observation*

Someone may have sighted the boat at the zero point at twelve o'clock and 28 miles south of that 2 hours later.   This is *one* observation; it leads to $\hat{\gamma} = {}^{28}\!/_2 = 14$ miles per hour southward as the maximum likelihood estimate of the river's speed.   The number of hours elapsed from the beginning to the end of the observation could have been 1 or ½ or 7 or anything else.

2. *A sample of several independent observations*

We may have several observations like the above but made on different days.   For instance,

OBSERVATION	TIME ELAPSED	DISTANCE TRAVELED
1	2 hours	28 miles south
2	4 hours	12 miles south
3	17 hours	44 miles south

3. *Several interdependent observations*

Observations may overlap; as, for example,

OBSERVATION	TIME OF OBSERVATION	DISTANCE TRAVELED
a	12 to 2 P.M.	28 miles south
b	1 to 5 P.M.	20 miles south
	of the same day	

Or information may come in even more complicated ways.   The likelihood function can be constructed only if we know both the *circumstances* of our observations and the readings derived from them. Cases 1, 2, and 3 lead to different likelihood functions because the circumstances differ.   Two observers, each of whom watched the boat for 2 consecutive hours unbeknownst to the other, would set up two likelihood functions *identical in form* into which they would feed *different readings*.   But each investigator would set up one and only one likelihood function.   This is a function of a *single sample, the* sample, *his* sample; no matter how independent, complicated, or interdependent his observations may be, they form a single sample. The maximum likelihood criterion tells us to proceed as if Nature did the most probable thing.   We assert this about the *totality* of observations in the sample rather than about any single observation.

2.4. The form of the likelihood function

Return to the consumption model $C_t = \alpha + \gamma Z_t + u_t$.   The following statement must be accepted on faith (its proof is a deepish theorem in analysis): Under the assumptions that Nature conforms to the model and that the true values of the parameters are α and γ, the probability of observing the particular sample $C_1, C_2, \ldots, C_S$, $Z_1, Z_2, \ldots, Z_S$ is equal to the probability that the error term shall have assumed the particular values $u_1, u_2, \ldots, u_S$ multiplied by a factor det $\mathbf{J}$.

The term det $\mathbf{J}$ happens to be equal to 1 in all single-equation cases; so we need not worry about it yet.   It becomes important in two-or-more-equation models.

The statement cited above is of immense and curious significance. We observe the sample C_s, Z_s.   But we cannot know *directly* how probable or improbable it is to obtain this particular sample, since all our stochastic assumptions have to do with the probability distribution of the u's, not of the C's and Z's.   On the other hand, we can never observe the random errors themselves.   So one might despair of finding the probability of this particular sample but for the remarkable property cited.   Let L stand for the probability of the sample and q for the probability that the random term will take on the values $u_1, u_2, \ldots, u_S$.   Then we have

$$L = \det \mathbf{J} \cdot q(u_1, u_2, \ldots, u_S) \qquad (2\text{-}3)$$

Now, the (unobservable) u's are functions of the (observed) C's and Z's and of (the unknown) α and γ, because the model implies

$u_t = C_t - \alpha - \gamma Z_t$. To *maximize likelihood* is to seek the pair of values of α and γ that makes L as large as possible.

What form $q(u_1, \ldots, u_S)$ takes depends on the stochastic assumptions about the error term.

This concludes the discussion of the *logic* behind maximum likelihood estimating of α and γ.

In the next few pages I discuss the *mechanism* of maximizing L under the Six Simplifying Assumptions. On a first reading, you might skip the rest of this section without serious loss. Readers who wish to refresh your manipulative skills, read on! We shall now omit writing det $\mathbf{J} = 1$, since we are discussing only single-equation cases at this point.

By Simplifying Assumption 4, the random terms $u_1, u_2, \ldots, u_S$ come from a multivariate normal distribution. Therefore (2-2) applies, and

$$L = q(u_1, u_2, \ldots, u_S) = (2\pi)^{-S/2} \det (\sigma_{\mathbf{uu}})^{-\frac{1}{2}}$$
$$\exp \left[-\tfrac{1}{2}(\mathbf{u} - \varepsilon\mathbf{u})(\sigma_{\mathbf{uu}})^{-1}(\mathbf{u} - \varepsilon\mathbf{u}) \right] \quad (2\text{-}4)$$

By Simplifying Assumption 2, $\varepsilon u_t = 0$. Simplifying Assumption 3 states that all diagonal elements of $\sigma_{\mathbf{uu}}$ are equal to a finite constant σ_{uu}, and Assumption 5 states that all nondiagonal elements are zero; so

$$\det (\sigma_{\mathbf{uu}})^{-\frac{1}{2}} = (\sigma_{uu})^{-S/2}$$

Therefore, (2-4) reduces to

$$L = (2\pi)^{-S/2}(\sigma_{uu})^{-S/2} \exp \left[-\tfrac{1}{2}\mathbf{u} \begin{pmatrix} \sigma_{uu} & \cdots & 0 \\ 0 & \cdots & 0 \\ 0 & \cdots & \sigma_{uu} \end{pmatrix}^{-1} \mathbf{u} \right]$$

and finally to

$$L = (2\pi)^{-S/2}(\sigma_{uu})^{-S/2} \exp \left[-\tfrac{1}{2}(\sigma_{uu})^{-1} \sum_{s=1}^{S} u_s^2 \right] \quad (2\text{-}5)$$

The following properties of L will not be proved:

1. L is a continuous function with respect to α, γ, σ_{uu} except at $\sigma_{uu} = 0$. This means that it can be differentiated quite safely. As for the exception, we need not worry about it; for u, as a random variable, assumes at least two distinct values in the universe, and

therefore $\sigma_{uu} > 0$. If the sample is of only two observations, the fit is perfect; m_{uu} is zero—but in that case we do not use the likelihood approach at all. We just solve the two equations $C_1 = \alpha + \gamma Z_1$ and $C_2 = \alpha + \gamma Z_2$ for the two unknowns α and γ.

2. Setting the partial derivatives of L equal to zero locates its maxima. It has no minimum; therefore, we do not need to worry about second-order conditions of maximization.

3. L is a maximum when its logarithm is a maximum. So, instead of (2-5), we maximize the more convenient expression

$$\log L = -\frac{S}{2} \log 2\pi - \frac{S}{2} \log \sigma_{uu} - \frac{1}{2} (\sigma_{uu})^{-1} \sum u_s^2 \qquad (2\text{-}6)$$

4. The true values of α, γ, and σ_{uu} are not functions of one another, but constants. Therefore, in maximizing, all partial derivatives of α, γ, and σ with respect to one another are zero.

Maximizing (2-6) results in

$$\sum (C_s - \alpha - \gamma Z_s) = 0$$
$$\sum (C_s - \alpha - \gamma Z_s) Z_s = 0 \qquad (2\text{-}7)$$
$$\frac{1}{S} \sum (C_s - \alpha - \gamma Z_s)^2 = \sigma_{uu}$$

The solution of (2-7) for α, γ, σ_{uu} gives the maximum likelihood estimate $\hat{\alpha}$, $\hat{\gamma}$, $\hat{\sigma}$.

2.5. Justification of the least squares technique

It is evident that (2-6) gives least squares estimates for α, γ, σ.

System (2-7) says that the maximum likelihood values of α and γ are the values that minimize the sum of the squares of the residuals $\hat{u}_s$. The last equation in (2-7) states that the maximum likelihood estimate $\hat{\sigma}_{uu}$ of the true variance σ_{uu} is the average square residual.

This, then, is the justification for minimizing squares. Remember that to get this result we had to make use of a great many assumptions both about the model itself and about the nature of its error term. If any one of these many assumptions had not been granted, we might not have reached this result. Therefore, one should not go about minimizing squares too lightheartedly.   For every different set of assumptions a certain estimating procedure is best, and least squares is best only with a proper combination of assumptions.   Conversely, every estimating procedure contains in itself (implicitly) some assumptions either about the model, or about the distribution of u, or both.[1]

Digression on computational arrangement

It pays to develop a tidy scheme for computing $\hat{\alpha}$, $\hat{\gamma}$, and $\hat{\sigma}_{uu}$ because computation recipes similar to (2-7) turn up pretty often.

It is always possible to arrange the computations in such a way as to estimate the coefficient γ of the independent variable first.   With $\hat{\gamma}$ in hand, one computes the constant term $\hat{\alpha}$. Finally, with $\hat{\alpha}$ and $\hat{\gamma}$, one computes the residuals $\hat{u}_s$, and from these residuals, an estimate of σ_{uu}.

An analogous procedure for models having several independent variables (and, hence, several γs) is developed in the next digression.

In all cases, that is to say, for simple as well as for complicated models, I shall describe only the computational steps for estimating the γs (coefficients of the independent variables).

Write (2-7) as follows:

$$\alpha S + \gamma \Sigma Z_s = \Sigma C_s$$
$$\alpha \Sigma Z_s + \gamma \Sigma Z_s^2 = \Sigma C_s Z_s$$

where the sums run over the entire sample.   Now subtract ΣZ_s times the first equation from S times the second.   The result is

$$\gamma[S\Sigma Z^2 - (\Sigma Z)(\Sigma Z)] = [S\Sigma CZ - (\Sigma C)(\Sigma Z)] \qquad (2\text{-}8)$$

Note that we have eliminated α and that, moreover, in the square brackets we may recognize the familiar *moments*, defined in Chap. 1.   Thus (2-8) is equivalent to

---

[1] The Six Simplifying Assumptions are sufficient but not necessary conditions for least squares.   Least squares is a "best linear unbiased estimator" under much simpler conditions.   This, however, is another subject.   I chose these particular six assumptions because with them it is easy to show how a stochastic specification and an estimating criterion lead to a specific estimate of a parameter rather than to some other estimate.

$$\gamma m_{ZZ} = m_{CZ}$$

and the estimate of γ can be expressed very simply as

$$\hat{\gamma} = (m_{ZZ})^{-1}m_{ZC} \qquad \text{or} \qquad \frac{m_{ZC}}{m_{ZZ}} \qquad\qquad (2\text{-}9)$$

which, besides being compact, generalizes easily to N dimensions, i.e., by replacing the Greek and italic letters by the corresponding characters in boldface type:

$$\hat{\boldsymbol{\gamma}} = (\mathbf{m}_{ZZ})^{-1}\mathbf{m}_{ZC} \qquad \text{or} \qquad \frac{\mathbf{m}_{ZC}}{\mathbf{m}_{ZZ}} \qquad\qquad (2\text{-}9a)$$

2.6. Generalized least squares

All the principles discussed so far apply to all linear models consisting of a single equation. To treat the general case, we shall make a slight change in notation: y will stand for any endogenous variable (the role played by consumption C so far) and z for any exogenous variable (the role played by lagged income Z so far).

Let us suppose that the endogenous variable $y(t)$ depends on H different predetermined variables $z_1(t)$, $z_2(t)$, . . . , $z_H(t)$ as follows (omitting time indexes):

$$y = \alpha + \gamma_1 z_1 + \gamma_2 z_2 + \cdots + \gamma_H z_H + u \qquad\qquad (2\text{-}10)$$

Indeed, the analogy of (2-10) with $C = \alpha + \gamma Z + u$ is so perfect that everything said about the latter applies to the shorthand edition of (2-10):

$$y = \alpha + \boldsymbol{\gamma}\mathbf{z} + u$$

where $\boldsymbol{\gamma}$ is the vector $(\gamma_1, \gamma_2, \ldots, \gamma_H)$ and $\mathbf{z}$ is the vector[1] $(z_1, z_2, \ldots, z_H)$.

But we must be careful. The first five Simplifying Assumptions (u is random, has mean zero, has constant variance, is normal, and is serially independent) need no alteration. Assumption 6 must, however, be changed to read as follows: The error term u_t is fully independent of $z_1(t)$, $z_2(t)$, . . . , $z_H(t)$.

Under the new version of the Simplifying Assumptions, the maxi-

[1] For typographical simplicity I shall not bother, in obvious cases, to distinguish a column from a row vector. In this case $\mathbf{z}$ is a column vector.

mum likelihood criterion leads to the estimate of $\gamma_1, \gamma_2, \ldots, \gamma_H$ that minimizes the sum of the squared residuals. And, moreover, these estimates are given by the formula

$$\hat{\boldsymbol{\gamma}} = (\mathbf{m}_{zz})^{-1}\mathbf{m}_{zy} \tag{2-11}$$

which is exactly analogous to (2-9). What these boldface symbols mean is explained in the next digression.

Digression on matrices of moments and their determinants

This is a natural place to introduce some extremely convenient notation, which we shall be using from Chap. 6 on.

If p, q, r, x, y are variables, $\mathbf{m}_{(p,q,r)\cdot(x,y)}$ is the matrix whose elements are moments that can be constructed with p, q, r on x and y. The variables in the first parentheses correspond to the rows and those in the second to the columns. Thus,

$$\mathbf{m}_{(p,q,r)\cdot(x,y)} = \begin{bmatrix} m_{px} & m_{py} \\ m_{qx} & m_{qy} \\ m_{rx} & m_{ry} \end{bmatrix}$$

The middle dot in the subscript may be omitted.

Likewise, $\mathbf{m}_{zz}$ means the matrix whose elements are moments of the variables $z_1, z_2, \ldots, z_H$ on themselves:

$$\mathbf{m}_{zz} = \begin{bmatrix} m_{z_1z_1} & m_{z_1z_2} & \cdots & m_{z_1z_H} \\ m_{z_2z_1} & m_{z_2z_2} & \cdots & m_{z_2z_H} \\ \cdot & \cdot & & \cdot \\ \cdot & \cdot & & \cdot \\ \cdot & \cdot & & \cdot \\ m_{z_Hz_1} & m_{z_Hz_2} & \cdots & m_{z_Hz_H} \end{bmatrix}$$

and $\mathbf{m}_{zy}$ means

$$\begin{bmatrix} m_{z_1y} \\ m_{z_2y} \\ \cdot \\ \cdot \\ \cdot \\ m_{z_Hy} \end{bmatrix}$$

Every *square* matrix has a determinant.   So does every *square* matrix of moments, for instance, $\mathbf{m}_{zz}$; for the determinant of $\mathbf{m}$ we write det $\mathbf{m}$, perhaps with the appropriate subscripts det $\mathbf{m}_{zz}$, or det $\mathbf{m}_{(z_1,z_2,\ldots,z_H)(z_1,z_2,\ldots,z_H)}$.

But it is simpler to write m_{zz} instead of det $\mathbf{m}$ or det $\mathbf{m}_{zz}$; and we shall do this for compactness.   The lightface italic m in the expression m_{zz} indicates that the determinant is a simple number, like 2 or 16.17, and neither a vector nor a matrix of numbers (these are printed bold).

One way to estimate the coefficients $\gamma_1, \gamma_2, \ldots, \gamma_H$ is to perform the *matrix* operations given in (2-11).   Another way is by *Cramer's rule*, which calculates various *determinants* and computes

$$\hat{\gamma}_1 = \frac{m_{(y,z_2,\ldots,z_H)(z_1 z_2,\ldots,z_H)}}{m_{(z_1,z_2,\ldots,z_H)(z_1,z_2,\ldots,z_H)}}$$

$$\hat{\gamma}_2 = \frac{m_{(z_1,y,\ldots,z_H)(z_1,z_2,\ldots,z_H)}}{m_{(z_1,z_2,\ldots,z_H)(z_1,z_2,\ldots,z_H)}}$$

$$\cdot$$
$$\cdot \qquad\qquad\qquad\qquad\qquad (2\text{-}12)$$
$$\cdot$$

$$\hat{\gamma}_H = \frac{m_{(z_1,z_2,\ldots,y)(z_1,z_2,\ldots,z_H)}}{m_{(z_1,z_2,\ldots,z_H)(z_1,z_2,\ldots,z_H)}}$$

Both these ways are very cumbersome in practice for equations with more than three or four variables, unless we have ready programs on electronic computers.   Appendix B gives a stepwise technique for calculating $\hat{\gamma}_1, \hat{\gamma}_2, \ldots, \hat{\gamma}_H$ that can be used on an ordinary desk calculator.

Matrix inversion is discussed in Appendix A.

2.7. The meaning of unbiasedness

Let us discuss bias and unbiasedness by using the original model of consumption $C_t = \alpha + \gamma Z_t + u_t$ with the understanding that all conclusions hold true for the generalized single-equation model $y = \alpha + \gamma_1 z_1 + \cdots + \gamma_H z_H + u$.   Furthermore, we can restrict ourselves, with some exceptions, to the discussion of γ, because the statements to be made are also true of α.

Imagine that we obtain our guess $\hat{\gamma}$ of the parameter γ, violating none of the Simplifying Assumptions. The guess so chosen is the most likely in the circumstances. But this does not guarantee it to be equal to the true value γ. This is so because the observations C_s, Z_s we have to go on are just a sample. And in sampling anything can happen. Extremely atypical misleading samples are improbable but perfectly possible. So it makes sense to ask how far off the guess $\hat{\gamma}$ is likely to be from the true value γ.

Here it is very important to distinguish between (1) taking again and again a sample of size S, (2) taking bigger and bigger samples (one of each size). The first procedure is connected with the important statistical notion of *bias*, the second with that of *consistency*. Both procedures are ideal and impractical, because such samples must be taken from the universe (level III) and not merely from the population (level II). Therefore, even with infinite resources and infinite patience, the concepts are not operational.

Consider any estimating recipe (say, least squares). Choose a sample size, say, $S = 20$; draw (from the universe) *all possible* samples of size 20; for each sample compute (by least squares) the corresponding $\hat{\gamma}$; then average out these $\hat{\gamma}$s. If the average $\hat{\gamma}$ equals the true γ, then we say that the procedure of least squares is an *unbiased method* for estimating γ, or an *unbiased estimator* of γ, for sample size $S = 20$. Loosely, we might say that *on the average*, least squares gives a correct estimate of γ from samples of 20 observations.

In order to pin down firmly the concept of bias, I have constructed a purposely simple and exaggerated example. It involves just three time periods, very uneven disturbances from time period to time period, and a random disturbance that assumes just three different values. Yet this example illustrates all that could be shown with a larger and more realistic one.

Assume that the true values of the parameters we seek to estimate are $\alpha = 4$, $\gamma = 0.4$. Assume that the population consists of exactly 3 elements, labeled a, b, c, whose coordinates are given in Table 2.1 below; the three points are shown in Fig. 2. This population could have come from an infinite universe, but let us (for pedagogic reasons) deal with a finite universe that consists of the above three points a, b, c plus four more, which are named a', b', c', and c''. Every point of the universe is completely defined when we specify the random

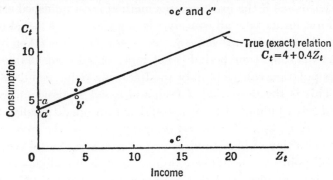

Fig. 2. A seven-point universe. Solid dots: points in the population. Hollow dots: points in the universe but not in the population.

Table 2.1
The population (a,b,c)

POINT	TIME p	Z_p	C_p	u_p
a	1	0	4.05	0.05
b	2	4	6	0.4
c	3	14	0.6	−9.0

error u that corresponds to it and the level of the independent **variable**. These are given in Table 2.2.

Table 2.2

TIME	POINTS IN THE POPULATION			POINTS IN THE UNIVERSE BUT NOT IN THE POPULATION		
	NAME	VALUE OF u_t	VALUE OF Z_t	NAME	VALUE OF u_t	VALUE OF Z_t
1	a	0.05	0	a'	−0.05	0
2	b	0.40	4	b'	−0.40	4
3	c	−9.00	14	c'	+4.50	14
3	...	......	...	c''	+4.50	14

Exercise

2.E   Which Simplifying Assumptions are fulfilled by u_t in the universe of Table 2.2, and which are violated?

Now let us see if the least squares method is an unbiased estimator of γ. First let us take all conceivable samples of size 2 and for each compute the least squares value $\hat{\gamma}$. Samples should be taken in such a way that the same time period is not represented more than once.

The population can yield only the following pairs: (a,b), (a,c), and (b,c). This is the most that a flesh-and-blood statistician, even one equipped with unlimited means, could obtain operationally, because points a', b', c', and c'' exist, so to speak, only in the mind of God. But the definition of bias requires us to check samples (of size 2) that include all points *of the universe*, human and divine alike. There are sixteen such samples, and the corresponding estimates $\hat{\alpha}$ and $\hat{\gamma}$ are given in Table 2.3 and plotted in Fig. 3. When all sixteen are considered, it is seen that least squares is an unbiased estimator of γ (and of α).

Table 2.3
Estimates of α and γ from samples of size 2

POINTS IN THE SAMPLE	CORRESPONDING ESTIMATE	
	OF γ	OF α
a b	0.4875	4.0500
a b'	0.2875	4.0500
a c	−0.2464	4.0498
a c'	0.7179	4.0497
a c''	0.7179	4.0497
a' b	0.5125	3.9500
a' b'	0.3125	3.9500
a' c	−0.2393	3.9501
a' c'	0.7250	3.9500
a' c''	0.7250	3.9500
b c	−0.5400	8.1600
b c'	0.8100	2.7600
b c''	0.8100	2.7600
b' c	−0.4600	7.0400
b' c'	0.8900	1.6400
b' c''	0.8900	1.6400
Average of all conceivable samples	$\varepsilon\hat{\gamma} =$ 0.4000	$\varepsilon\hat{\alpha} =$ 4.0000
Average of all feasible samples (unprimed points)	−0.0997	5.4199

If we try all samples of size 3, we get the results tabulated in Table 2.4 and plotted in Fig. 4.

Table 2.4
Estimates of α and γ from samples of size 3

POINTS IN THE SAMPLE	$\hat{\alpha}$	$\hat{\gamma}$
a b c	5.36728	−0.30288
a b c'	3.63652	0.73558
a b c''	3.63652	0.73558
a b' c	5.00833	−0.28750
a b' c'	3.27757	0.75096
a b' c''	3.27757	0.75096
a' b c	5.29939	−0.29712
a' b c'	3.56857	0.74135
a' b c''	3.56857	0.74135
a' b' c	4.94038	−0.28173
a' b c'	3.20962	0.75673
a' b' c''	3.20962	0.75673
Average	$\varepsilon\hat{\alpha} = 4.0000$	$\varepsilon = 0.4000$

For a sample of size 3, the least squares method is an unbiased estimator of both γ and α.

In certain cases, not illustrated by our simple example, (1) an estimating technique (say, least squares) may be unbiased for some sample sizes and biased for other sizes; (2) a method may overestimate γ for certain sample sizes and underestimate it for others, on the average; (3) we may be able to tell *a priori*, knowing the sample size S, whether the bias is positive or negative (in other cases we cannot); (4) a method may be unbiased for one parameter but biased for another.

2.8. Variance of the estimate

In Fig. 3 I have plotted all the estimates of α and γ for all possible samples of size 2. The same thing was done for size 3 in Fig. 4. In general, the estimates are scattered or clustered, depending (1) on the size S of the sample, (2) on the size and other features of the universe, (3) on the particular estimating technique we have adopted, and ultimately (4) on the extent to which random effects dominate the systematic variables. Other things being equal, we prefer an estimating technique that yields clustered estimates. The spread among the various estimates $\hat{\gamma}$ is called the *variance of the estimate* $\hat{\gamma}$, and is written $\sigma_{\hat{\gamma}\hat{\gamma}}$ or $\sigma(\hat{\gamma},\hat{\gamma})$, or, sometimes, $\sigma(\hat{\gamma},\hat{\gamma}|S)$ if we want to emphasize what size sample it relates to.

The variance is defined by

$$\sigma(\hat{\gamma},\hat{\gamma}) \;=\; \varepsilon(\hat{\gamma} - \varepsilon\hat{\gamma})^2$$

and is a constant, which exists and can be computed if the four items listed above are known. Table 2.5 gives the values of σ for our

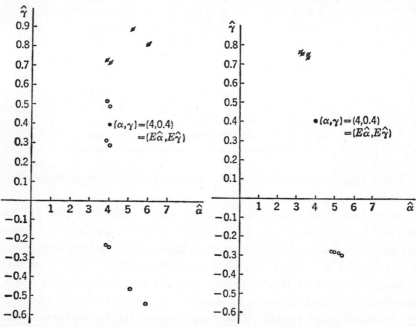

Fig. 3. Parameter estimates from all samples of size 2. ϕ: double point.

Fig. 4. Parameter estimates from all samples of size 3. ϕ: double point.

seven-point example. Note the interesting (and counterintuitive) fact that the variance of the estimate can increase as the sample size increases! This quirk arises because, in the example, the random disturbance has a skew distribution. If u is symmetrical, the variance of the estimate decreases as the sample size increases.

Table 2.5

Size S of samples	$\sigma(\hat{\gamma},\hat{\gamma})$
2	0.2325
3	0.2397

2.9. Estimates of the variance of the estimate

If we have complete knowledge, we can compute the true value of $\sigma(\hat{\gamma},\hat{\gamma}|S)$ by making a complete list of all samples of size S, computing all possible estimates of γ, and finding their variance, as I did in the above example.   In practice, however, it is impossible to exhaust all samples of a given size, because the universe contains points that are not in the population.   So, instead, we must be content with guessing at the variance of the estimate by the use of whatever information is contained in the single sample we have already drawn.

At first, you might suppose that estimating $\sigma(\hat{\gamma},\hat{\gamma}|S)$ is logically impossible when you have *a single sample* of size S to work with, because, after all, the variance of the estimate of γ represents what happens to γ as you take *all samples* of size S.

All is not lost, however, because a single sample of size S contains several samples (S of them) each of size S-minus-1.   The latter we can generate by leaving out, one at a time, each observation of the original sample.   Thus, if the original sample is (a,b,c) of size $S = 3$, it contains three subsamples of size 2 each, the following ones: (a,b), (a,c), and (b,c), which yield, respectively, the three estimates $\hat{\gamma}(a,b)$, $\hat{\gamma}(a,c)$, and $\hat{\gamma}(b,c)$.   We get, then, some idea about variations in the estimate of γ *among samples of size 2*.   Still, we know nothing about the variance of γ as estimated *from samples of size 3*.   Here we invoke the maximum likelihood criterion.   The original sample (a,b,c) was assumed to be *the most probable* of its kind, namely, the family of samples containing three observations each.   If this is so, then observations a, b, c generate the *most probable triplet* $\mathbf{T} = \{(a,b),(a,c),(b,c)\}$ of samples containing two observations each.   Therefore, the variability of $\hat{\gamma}$ (*in the triplet* $\mathbf{T}$) estimates its variability in samples of size 3.

From Table 2.3,

$$\hat{\gamma}(a,b) = 0.4875$$
$$\hat{\gamma}(a,c) = -0.2464$$
$$\hat{\gamma}(b,c) = -0.5400$$
$$\text{Average} = -0.0997$$

The variance of $\hat{\gamma}$ in the sample triplet is equal to

$$\tfrac{1}{3}[(0.4875 + 0.0997)^2 + (-0.2464 + 0.0997)^2$$
$$+ (-0.5400 + 0.0997)^2] = 0.1867$$

The last figure must now be corrected by the factor S-minus-1 $= 2$ if it is to be an unbiased estimate of the variance of $\hat{\gamma}(a,b,c)$. Estimates of variance based on *averages*, if uncorrected, naturally understate the variance. The proof that

$$\hat{\sigma} = 0.1867 \times 2 = 0.3734$$

is an unbiased estimate of $\sigma(\hat{\gamma},\hat{\gamma}|3)$ is in Appendix C.

In practice we are too lazy to estimate γ again and again for all the subsamples. The formula $\bar{\sigma}(\hat{\gamma},\hat{\gamma}|S) = m_{\hat{u}\hat{u}}/(S-1)m_{zz}$ gives a short-cut (and biased) estimate of the variance of $\hat{\gamma}$ for samples of the original size. Table 2.6 lists these estimates for three-point samples and repeats some of the information from Table 2.4.

Table 2.6
Estimates of γ and of the variance of its estimates

POINTS IN THE SAMPLE	$\hat{\gamma}$	$\bar{\sigma}(\hat{\gamma},\hat{\gamma}) = \dfrac{m_{\hat{u}\hat{u}}}{(S-1)m_{zz}}$
$a\ \ b\ \ c$	-0.30288	0.02605
$a\ \ b\ \ c'$	0.73558	0.00256
$a\ \ b\ \ c''$	0.73558	0.00256
$a\ \ b'\ c$	-0.28750	0.01377
$a\ \ b'\ c'$	0.75096	0.00895
$a\ \ b'\ c''$	0.75096	0.00895
$a'\ b\ \ c$	-0.29712	0.02731
$a'\ b\ \ c'$	0.74135	0.00217
$a'\ b\ \ c''$	0.74135	0.00217
$a'\ b'\ c$	-0.28173	0.01377
$a'\ b'\ c'$	0.75673	0.00822
$a'\ b'\ c''$	0.75673	0.00822

Table 2.6 must be interpreted carefully. To begin with, the investigator will usually know only its first line, because he has a single sample to work with. The remaining lines are put in Table 2.6, for pedagogic reasons, by the omniscient being who can consider all possible worlds. Events could have followed one or another course (and only one) among the courses listed in the several lines of Table 2.6. It just happened that (a,b,c) materialized and not some other triplet. It yielded the two estimates $\hat{\gamma} = -0.30288$, a very wrong estimate, and $\bar{\sigma} = 0.02605$. The latter misleads us to believe in the likelihood of the former.

If sample (a',b',c') had materialized, the two guesses would have been $\hat{\gamma} = 0.73558$ (not so bad as before) and $\bar{\sigma} = 0.00256$, which is ten times as "confident" as before. It is entirely possible for a sample to give a very wrong parameter estimate with a great deal of confidence. The mere fact that $\bar{\sigma}(\hat{\gamma},\hat{\gamma})$ is small does not make $\hat{\gamma}$ a good guess.

It is comforting, of course, to have some measure of how much $\hat{\gamma}$ varies from sample to sample. What is upsetting is that the measure is itself a *guess*. True, it is better than nothing, but this is no consolation if by some quirk of fate we have picked a sample so atypical that it gives us not only a really wrong parameter estimate $\hat{\gamma}$, but also a really small $\bar{\sigma}(\hat{\gamma},\hat{\gamma})$. The moral is: Don't be cocksure about the excellence of your guess of γ just because you have guessed that its variance $\sigma(\hat{\gamma},\hat{\gamma})$ is small.

2.10. Estimates *ad nauseam*

Note carefully now that, whereas $\sigma(\hat{\gamma},\hat{\gamma})$ is a constant, $\bar{\sigma}(\hat{\gamma},\hat{\gamma})$ is not, but varies with each sample of the given size. Therefore $\bar{\sigma}(\hat{\gamma},\hat{\gamma})$ itself has a variance, which we may denote by $\sigma(\bar{\sigma}(\hat{\gamma},\hat{\gamma}))$; this is a true constant. Now there is nothing to prevent us from making a guess at the latter on the basis of our sample, and this guess would be symbolized by $\bar{\sigma}(\bar{\sigma}(\hat{\gamma},\hat{\gamma}))$, which is no longer a constant but varies with each sample, and so has a true variance $\sigma(\bar{\sigma}(\bar{\sigma}(\hat{\gamma},\hat{\gamma})))$—and so on, ad infinitum. In other words, we cannot get away from the fact that, if all we can do about γ is to guess that it equals $\hat{\gamma}$, then all we can do about its variance $\sigma(\hat{\gamma},\hat{\gamma})$ is to guess *it* too; likewise all we can do about this last guess is to guess again about its true variance, and so on forever. Guess we must, stage after stage, unless we have some outside knowledge. Only with outside knowledge can the guessing game stop. The game is rarely played, however, beyond $\bar{\sigma}(\hat{\gamma},\hat{\gamma})$, (1) because it is quite tedious, and (2) because large enough samples give good $\hat{\gamma}$s and $\bar{\sigma}$s with high probability.

2.11. The meaning of consistency

As in our explanation of unbiasedness, let us discuss the parameter γ of the model $C_t = \alpha + \gamma Z_t + u_t$ with the understanding that all conclusions generalize to all the parameters in the model

$$y = \alpha + \gamma_1 z_1 + \cdots + \gamma_H z_H + u$$

Consider any estimating recipe, say, least squares or least cubes. Choose a sample of a given size, say, $S = 20$, and compute $\hat{\gamma}$. Then choose another sample containing one more observation ($S = 21$) and compute its $\hat{\gamma}$. Keep doing this, always increasing the sample's size. The bigger samples do not have to include any elements of the smaller samples—though this becomes inevitable as the big samples grow, if the universe is finite.[1]   If, as the size of the sample grows, the estimates $\hat{\gamma}$ improve, then we say that the least squares procedure is a *consistent estimator* of γ.   Note that $\hat{\gamma}$ does not have to improve in each and every step of this process of increasing the size of the sample.

Improvement in the above paragraph means that the probability distributions of $\hat{\gamma}(S)$, $\hat{\gamma}(S + 1)$, . . . become more and more pinched as they straddle the true value of the parameter.

Digression on notation

There are two variant notations for consistency.   Let $\tilde{\gamma}(s)$ be the consistent estimator from a sample of s observations.   Let ϵ and η be two positive numbers, however small.   Then there is some size S for which

$$P(|\tilde{\gamma}(s) - \gamma| < \epsilon) > 1 - \eta$$

if $s > S$.   A shorthand notation for the same thing is

$$P \lim \tilde{\gamma}(s) = \gamma$$

which is to be read "$\tilde{\gamma}(s)$ converges to γ in probability," or "probability limit of $\tilde{\gamma}(s)$ is γ."

Under very weak restrictions, a maximum likelihood estimate is also a consistent estimate.   Note, however, that, even when the method is consistent, there is no guarantee that the estimate will improve every time we take a larger sample.   It may turn out that our sample of size 2 happens to contain points a and b, which give an estimate $\tilde{\gamma}(2) = 0.4875$, and the next larger sample happens to contain points

---

[1] A sample could, of course, be infinite without ever including all the elements of an infinite universe.

a, b, and c, which give an estimate $\hat{\gamma}(3) = -0.30288$, which is much worse.   Even when the larger sample includes all the points of the smaller, as in the example just cited, it can give a worse estimate. This is so because the next point drawn, c, may be so atypical as to outweigh the previous typical points a and b.

2.12. The merits of unbiasedness and consistency

Are the properties of unbiasedness and consistency worth the fuss? Remember the fundamental fact that with limited sampling resources it is not possible to estimate γ correctly every time, even when the estimating procedure is unbiased and consistent.

Because of a small budget, our sample may be so small that $\hat{\gamma}$ has a large variance.   Even if the sample is large, it may be an unlucky one, yielding an extremely wrong estimate.   The mistake has happened, and it is no consolation to know that, if we had taken all possible samples of that size, we would have hit the correct estimate on the average.   The following complaint is a familiar one from the area of Uncertainty Economics: Some people advise me to behave always so as to maximize my expected utility; in other words, to make once-in-a-lifetime decisions as if I had an eternity to repeat the experiment. Well, if I get my head chopped off on the first (and necessarily final) try, what do I care about the theoretical average consequences of my decision?   Wherever a comparatively *crucial* outcome hinges on a *single* correct estimate, unbiasedness is not in itself a desirable property.

Likewise, it is mockery to tell an unsuccessful econometrician that he could have improved his estimate if he had been willing to enlarge his sample indefinitely.

What, then, is the use of unbiasedness and consistency?   In themselves they are of no use; they do help, however, in the design of samples and as rules for research strategy and communication among investigators.

There is a body of statistical theory—not discussed in this work— which tells us how to redesign our sample in order to decrease bias and inconsistency to some tolerable level.   For example, with infinite universe, if we have two parameters to estimate, the theory says that a sample must be larger than 100 if consistency is to become "effective at the 5 per cent level."   Whether we want to take a sample that large depends on the use and strategic importance of our estimate as well as on the cost of sampling. All this opens up the fields of verification and statistical decision, into which we shall not go here.

Unbiasedness, consistency, and other estimating criteria to be introduced below are sometimes conceived of as *scientific conventions:*[1]

If content to look at the procedure of point estimation unpretentiously as a social undertaking, we may therefore state our criterion of preference for a method of agreement so conceived in the following terms:

  (i) different observers make at different times observations of one and the same thing by one and the same method;

 (ii) individual sets of observations so conceived are independent samples of *possible observations consistent with a framework of competence,* and as such we may tentatively conceptualise the performance of successive sets as a stochastic process;

(iii) we shall then prefer any method of combining constituents of observations, if it is such as to ensure a higher probability of agreement between successive sets, as the size of the sample enlarges in accordance with the assumption that we should thereby reach the true value of the unknown quantity in the limit;

 (iv) for a given sample size, we shall also prefer a method of combination which guarantees minimum dispersion of values obtainable by different observers within the framework of (i) above.

In the long run, the convention last stated guarantees that there will be a minimum of disagreement between the observations of different observers, if they all pursue the same rule consistently. . . . We have undertaken to operate within a fixed framework of repetition. This is an assumption which is intelligible in the domain of surveying, of astronomy or of experimental physics. How far it is meaningful in the domain of biology and whether it is ever meaningful in the domain of the social sciences are questions which we cannot lightly dismiss by the emotive appeal of the success or usefulness of statistical methods in the observatory, in the physical laboratory and in the cartographer's office.

Philosophers of probability are still debating whether the italics of the quotation do in fact define a universe of sampling, whether it can be defined apart from the postulate that an Urn of Nature underlies everything, and whether the above scientific conventions become reasonable only upon our conceding the postulate.

---

[1] Lancelot Hogben, *Statistical Theory*, pp. 206–207 (London: George Allen & Unwin, Ltd., 1957). Italics added.

2.13. Other estimating criteria

So far I have mentioned three estimating criteria, or properties that we might desire our estimating procedures to have. These were (1) maximum likelihood, (2) unbiasedness, (3) consistency. Some others are:

4. *Efficiency*

If $\tilde{\gamma}$ and $\hat{\gamma}$ are two estimators from a sample of S observations, the more efficient one has the smaller variance. It is possible to have $\sigma(\tilde{\gamma},\tilde{\gamma}) < \sigma(\hat{\gamma},\hat{\gamma})$ for some sample sizes and the reverse for other sample sizes; or one may be *uniformly more efficient* than the other; some estimators are *most efficient*, others *uniformly most efficient*.

5. *Sufficiency*

An estimator from a sample of size S is sufficient if no other estimator *from the same sample* can add any knowledge about the parameter being estimated. For instance, to estimate the population mean, the sample mean is sufficient and the sample median is not.

6. The following desirable property has no name. Let $\sigma(\hat{\gamma},\hat{\gamma}|S)$ shrink more rapidly than $\sigma(\tilde{\gamma},\tilde{\gamma}|S)$ as the sample increases. Then $\hat{\gamma}$ is more desirable than $\tilde{\gamma}$.

There is no end to the criteria one might invent. Nor are the criteria listed mutually exclusive. Indeed, a maximum likelihood estimator tends to the normal distribution as the sample increases; it is consistent and most efficient for large samples. A maximum likelihood estimator from a single-peaked, symmetrically distributed universe is unbiased.

2.14. Least squares and the criteria

If all the Simplifying Assumptions are satisfied, the least squares method of estimating α and γ in single-equation models of the form

$$C_t = \alpha + \gamma Z_t + u_t \qquad (2\text{-}13)$$

yields maximum likelihood, unbiased, consistent, efficient, and sufficient estimates of the parameters. This result can be generalized

in a variety of directions.   The first generalization is that it applies to
a model of the form

$$y(t) = \alpha + \gamma_1 z_1(t) + \gamma_2 z_2(t) + \cdots + \gamma_H z_H(t) + u(t) \quad (2\text{-}14)$$

where y is the endogenous variable and the z's are *exogenous* variables.
(Least squares is biased if some of the z's are *lagged* values of y—this
question is postponed to the next chapter.)

Least squares yields maximum likelihood, unbiased, consistent,
sufficient, but *inefficient* estimates if the variance of u_t is not constant
but varies systematically, either with time or with the magnitude of
the exogenous variables.   Such systematic variation of its variance
makes u *heteroskedastic*.

2.15. Treatment of heteroskedasticity

We shall confine the discussion of heteroskedasticity to model
(2-13) on the understanding that it generalizes to (2-14).

The random term can have a variable variance $\sigma_{uu}(t)$ for various
reasons:

1. People learn, and so their errors of behavior become absolutely
smaller with time.   In this case $\sigma(t)$ decreases.

2. Income grows, and people now barely discern dollars whereas
previously they discerned dimes.   Here $\sigma(t)$ grows.

3. As income grows, errors of measurement also grow, because now
the tax returns, etc., from which C and Z are measured no longer
report pennies.   Here $\sigma(t)$ increases.

4. Data-collecting techniques improve. $\sigma(t)$ decreases.

Consider Fig. 5.   It shows a sample of three points coming from a
heteroskedastic universe.

Since the errors are heteroskedastic, we would, on the average,
expect observations in range 1 to fall rather near the true regression
line, observations in range 2 somewhat farther, and in range 3 farther
still.   In any given sample, say, (a,b,c), points b and c should ideally
be "discounted" according to the greater variances that prevail in
their ranges.   Using the straight sum of squares is the same as failing
to discount b and c.   The result is that sample (a,b,c) gives a larger
value for γ than it would if observations had been properly discounted.

If no allowance is made for the changing variance $\sigma(t)$, least squares fits are maximum likelihood, unbiased, and consistent but inefficient. To show inefficiency, consider the likelihood function of (2-4). There, the matrix σ of the covariances of the random term not only was diagonal but had equal entries; so it could factor out [see (2-5)] and drop out when the likelihood function was maximized with respect to γ (and α). It is this fact that made $\hat{\gamma}$ an efficient estimate. With unequal entries along the diagonal, this is no longer possible. To obtain an efficient, unbiased, and consistent estimate of γ, we must solve a complicated set of equations involving γ, $\sigma(1)$, . . . , $\sigma(S)$. Somewhat less efficient (but more so than minimizing Σu^2) is to make

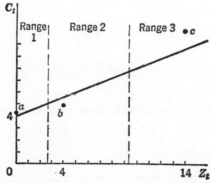

Fig. 5. A typical sample from a heteroskedastic universe.

(from outside knowledge) approximate guesses about $\sigma(1)$, . . . , $\sigma(S)$ and to minimize the sum of squares of appropriately "deflated" residuals (see Exercise 2.G). This, too, is an unbiased and consistent estimate.

Exercises

2.F Prove that $\hat{\gamma} = m_{ZC}/m_{ZZ}$ is unbiased and consistent even when u is heteroskedastic.

2.G Let $\phi(s)$ be an estimate (from outside information) of $1/\sigma_{uu}(s)$. Prove that minimizing $\Sigma\phi(s)u^2(s)$ yields the following estimate of γ:

$$\hat{\gamma}(\phi) = \frac{(\Sigma(\phi)\Sigma\phi CZ) - (\Sigma\phi Z)(\Sigma\phi C)}{(\Sigma\phi)(\Sigma\phi Z^2) - (\Sigma\phi Z)^2}$$

2.H Prove the unbiasedness and consistency of $\hat{\gamma}(\phi)$.

Digression on arbitrary weights

The weights $\phi(s)$ are arbitrary. Is there no danger that the denominator of $\hat{\gamma}(\phi)$ might be (nearly or exactly) zero and blow up the proceedings?

Answer: There is none.

Proof

$$\left(\sum \phi\right)\left(\sum \phi Z^2\right) - \left(\sum \phi Z\right)^2 = \sum_i \phi_i^2 Z_i^2 + \sum_i \phi_i \left(\sum_{j \neq i} \phi_j\right) Z_i^2$$

$$- \sum_i (\phi_i Z_i)^2 - 2 \sum_{i \neq j} \phi_i \phi_j Z_i Z_j$$

$$= \sum_{i \neq j} \phi_i \phi_j (Z_i^2 + Z_j^2 - 2Z_i Z_j)$$

$$= \sum_{i \neq j} \phi_i \phi_j (Z_i - Z_j)^2 > 0$$

It is perfectly proper to deflate the heteroskedastic residuals by the exogenous variable Z itself and to fit by least squares the homoskedastic equation

$$\frac{C}{Z} = \alpha \frac{1}{Z} + \gamma + \frac{u}{Z} \tag{2-15}$$

instead of the original heteroskedastic one

$$C = \alpha + \gamma Z + u \tag{2-16}$$

From (2-15) and (2-16) we obtain numerically different consistent and unbiased estimates of α and γ.

Exercise

2.1 Prove that $\hat{\alpha}(Z) = m_{(C/Z)(1/Z)}/m_{(1/Z)(1/Z)}$ is unbiased and consistent.

Further readings

Maurice G. Kendall, "On the Method of Maximum Likelihood" (*Journal of the Royal Statistical Society*, vol. 103, pt. 3, pp. 389–399, 1940) discusses the reasonableness of the method and the concept of likelihood. Whether the principle of maximum likelihood is logically wound up with *subjective belief* or *inverse probability* is still under debate. The intrepid reader who leafs through the last 30 or so years of the above *Journal* will be rewarded with the spectacle of a battle of nimble giants: Bartlett, Fisher, Gini, Jeffreys, Kendall, Keynes, Pearson, Yule.

The algebra of moments is a special application of matrices and vectors. Matrices and determinants are explained in the appendixes of KLEIN and TINTNER. ALLEN devotes two chapters (12 and 13) to all the vector, matrix, and determinant theory an economist is ever likely to need.

The estimating criteria of unbiasedness, consistency, etc., are clearly stated and briefly discussed in the first dozen pages of KENDALL's second volume, and debunked by Hogben in the reference cited in the text.

The reason for using $m_{\hat{u}\hat{u}}/Sm_{zz}$ as an estimate of $\sigma(\hat{\gamma},\hat{\gamma})$, the formulas for estimating cov $(\hat{a},\hat{\gamma})$ and $\sigma(\hat{a},\hat{a})$, and the extensions of these formulas for several γ variables are stated and rationalized (in my opinion, not too convincingly) by KLEIN, pp. 133–137.

CHAPTER 3

Bias in models of decay

3.1. Introduction and summary

This chapter is tedious and not crucial; it can be skipped without great loss. I wrote it for two reasons: to develop the concept of *conjugate samples,* and to show what I have claimed in the Preface: that common-sense interpretations of intricate theorems in mathematical statistics can be found.

The main proposition of this chapter is that a single-equation model of the form

$$y_t = y(t) = \alpha + \gamma_1 z_1(t) + \cdots + \gamma_H z_H(t) + u(t) \qquad (3\text{-}1)$$

in which some of the z's are not exogenous variables but rather lagged values of y itself, necessarily violates Simplifying Assumption 6, and hence that maximum likelihood estimates of α, γ_1, . . . , γ_H are biased.

The concept of *conjugate samples* gives a handy and simple-minded but entirely rigorous way to test for bias. It will be used again and again in later chapters for models much more complicated than (3-1).

Equations involving lags of an endogenous variable are called *autoregressive.*

Most satisfactory dynamic econometric models are multivariate autoregressive systems, in other words, elaborate versions of (3-1), and share its pitfalls in estimation. We shall see that the character of *initial conditions* affects vitally our estimating procedure and that, unfortunately, in econometrics the initial conditions are not favorable to estimation, though in the experimental sciences they commonly are.

If the initial condition $y(0)$ is a fixed constant Y, the maximum likelihood criterion leads to least squares regression of $y(t)$ on $y(t-1)$, and the resulting estimate for γ is biased, except for samples of size 1.

If $y(0)$ is a random variable, independent of u, then the maximum likelihood criterion does not lead to least squares. If least squares are used in this instance, they lead to biased estimates, again with the exception of samples of size 1.

CONVENTION

The size S of the sample is given in units that correspond to the number of points through which a line is fitted. Thus, if we observe only y_3 and y_2, this is a sample of *one; $S = 1$.* If we observe y_4, y_3, and y_2, this makes a sample of *two points*, $S = 2$, and so on. In his proof of this theorem, Hurwicz (in KOOPMANS, chap. 15) would call these, respectively, samples of size $T = 2$ and $T = 3$. The difference is important when observations have gaps (are not consecutive). We shall confine ourselves to consecutive samples. Appendix D deals with the general case.

3.2. Violation of Simplifying Assumption 6

A lagged variable, unlike an exogenous variable, cannot be independent of the random component of the model. In (3-1) a lagged value of y is necessarily correlated with some past value of u, because $y(t)$ and $u(t)$ are clearly correlated. Therefore, the very specification of (3-1) rules out Simplifying Assumption 6.

But why worry about such models? Because (3-1) and its generalizations express in linear form *oscillations*, *decay*, and *explosions*, which are all of great interest and which are, indeed, the bread and butter of physics, astronomy, and economics. For instance, springs behave substantially like

$$y(t) = \alpha + \gamma_1 y(t-1) + \gamma_2 y(t-2) + u(t)$$

and radioactive decay and pendulums like

$$y(t) = \gamma y(t-1) + u(t) \tag{3-2}$$

Business cycles are more complicated, involving several equations like (3-1).

Why do we want unbiased estimates? There are excellent reasons. If the world responds to our actions with some delay or if we respond with delay to the world, in order to act correctly we need to know the parameters accurately. How hot the water in the shower is now depends on how far I had turned the tap some seconds ago. If my estimate of the parameter expressing the response of water temperature to a turn of the tap is biased, this means that I freeze or get scalded or that I alternate between these two states, and, in any event, that I reach a comfortable temperature much later than I would with an unbiased estimate.

In economics, consumers, businesses, and governments act like a man in a shower. The information they get about prices, sales, orders, or national income comes with some delay and reflects the water temperature at the tap some time ago. Moreover, it takes time to decide and to put decisions into effect. If the decision makers have misjudged how strong are the natural damping properties of the economy, decisions and policy will either overshoot or undershoot the mark, or alternate between overshooting and undershooting it, and will cause uncomfortable and unnecessary oscillations in economic activity.

Our discussion will now be confined to the simplest possible case (3-2). Let consumption this year $y(t)$ depend on consumption last year $y(t-1)$, as in (3-2). If the relationship involved a constant term α, we eliminate α by measuring y not from the origin but from its equilibrium value. I shall illustrate my argument by a concrete example where the true γ has the convenient value 0.5 and where the initial value Y is fixed and equal to 24.

In Fig. 6, line OP represents the exact relationship $y_t = 0.5y_{t-1}$.

3.3. Conjugate samples

In model (3-1) with fixed initial conditions, we can describe a sample completely by mentioning two things: (1) what time periods it includes and (2) what values the disturbances took on *in those periods.* For example, (a,b,c,d) in Fig. 6 is completely described by

$$\begin{bmatrix} s = 1, & 2, & 3, & 4 \\ u_s = 4, & 0, & 0, & 0 \end{bmatrix}$$

(a',b',c',d') is described by

$$\begin{bmatrix} s = & 1, & 2, & 3, & 4 \\ u_s = & -4, & 0, & 0, & 0 \end{bmatrix}$$

and (a',b',d',e) by

$$\begin{bmatrix} s = & 1, & 2, & 4, & 5 \\ u_s = & -4, & 0, & 0, & 0 \end{bmatrix}$$

If u is symmetrically distributed, all conceivable samples of size S that one can draw from the universe can be arranged in *conjugate sets.* We shall see that *in each conjugate set* the maximum likelihood estimates

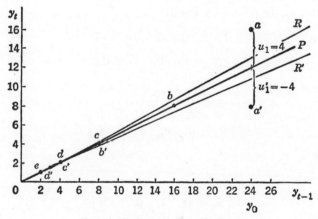

Fig. 6. Conjugate disturbances.

of γ average to less than the true value of γ and, therefore, that maximum likelihood estimates are biased for all samples of size S.

These propositions need to be qualified if $S = 1$ or if γ is not between 0 and 1; they are *proved* if $u(t)$ is normally distributed, but only *conjectured* if $u(t)$ has some other symmetrical distribution.

For an introduction to the concept of *conjugate samples,* consider

Fig. 6, which depicts two of the many possible courses that events can follow under our assumptions that $\gamma = 0.5$ and $Y = 24$. One course is represented by the points a, b, c, d, e, . . . ; the other by a', b', c', d', ... In the first course, the disturbance is equal to $+4$ in period 1 and zero thereafter. In the second course, it is -4 in period 1 and zero thereafter. The samples $\mathbf{S}(+) = (a,b,c,d)$ and $\mathbf{S}(-) = (a',b',c',d')$ are *conjugate samples*, and form a *conjugate set*. Similarly, (a,b,c) and (a',b',c') form a *conjugate set*.

To be *conjugate*, two samples must be drawn from the same time span $s = 1, 2, \ldots, S$; and the disturbances u_s that contributed to corresponding observations must have the same absolute value in the two samples. This definition is for consecutive samples only. Appendix D extends it to the nonconsecutive case.

Thus, sample

$$(d,e) = \begin{bmatrix} s = 4, & 5 \\ u_s = 0, & 0 \end{bmatrix}$$

forms a conjugate set all by itself.

$$\begin{bmatrix} s = 3, & 4, & 5, & 6 \\ u_s = 0, & 0, & 17, & 0 \end{bmatrix}$$

has as its conjugate

$$\begin{bmatrix} s = 3, & 4, & 5, & 6 \\ u_s = 0, & 0, & -17, & 0 \end{bmatrix}$$

Sample

$$\begin{bmatrix} s = 4, & 5, & 6, & 7 \\ u_s = 0, & 1, & 0, & -9 \end{bmatrix}$$

has three conjugates, the following:

$$\begin{bmatrix} s = 4, & 5, & 6, & 7 \\ u_s = 0, & -1, & 0, & -9 \end{bmatrix} \quad \begin{bmatrix} s = 4, & 5, & 6, & 7 \\ u_s = 0, & 1, & 0, & 9 \end{bmatrix}$$

$$\begin{bmatrix} s = 4, & 5, & 6, & 7 \\ u_s = 0, & -1, & 0, & 9 \end{bmatrix}$$

The greatest conjugate set of samples of size S is 2^k, where k ($0 \leq k \leq S$) represents the number of nonzero disturbances. If $S = 4$, the largest conjugate set contains 16 samples.

3.4. Source of bias

In Fig. 6, line OR with slope $\tilde{\gamma}[S(+)] = 0.6053$ is the least squares regression through the origin, and sample $S(+) = (a,b,c,d)$; and OR' with slope $\tilde{\gamma}[S(-)] = 0.3545$ is the same for the conjugate (a',b',c',d'). The line OR overestimates γ because OR is pulled up by point a. The line OR' underestimates γ because of the downward pull of point a'. As we have $\frac{1}{2}(0.6053 + 0.3545) = 0.4799 \leq \gamma$, the downward pull is the stronger. But why? Because point a is accompanied by b, c, d, and a' by b', c', d'. The primed points b', c', d' are closer to the origin than the corresponding unprimed points; hence, their "leverage" on their least squares line OR' is weaker than the leverage of the unprimed points on theirs (line OR). It is impossible for a' to be accompanied by b, c, d, because all future periods must necessarily inherit whatever impulse was first imparted by the random term of period 1. Points b', c', d' inherit a negative impulse, and points b, c, d inherit a positive one.

Another way of stating this is by referring to (3-1). In (3-1) one of the z's (say, z_4) is a lagged value of y (say, the lag is 2 time periods). It follows that $z_4(t)$ is correlated with the past value of the disturbance $u(t - 2)$, since $y(t)$ is clearly correlated with $u(t)$.

All the proofs of bias later in this chapter and in Appendix D are merely fancy versions of what I have just shown for this special case. When conjugate sets are large, arguments from the geometry of Fig. 6, though perfectly possible, become confusing, and so we turn to algebra.

With fixed initial condition $y(0) = Y$, the maximum likelihood estimate of γ is the least squares estimate

$$\tilde{\gamma} = \frac{\sum_s y_s y_{s-1}}{\sum_s y_{s-1}^2} \tag{3-3}$$

3.5. Extent of the bias

From (3-3) and (3-2),

$$\check{\gamma} = \gamma + \frac{\sum\limits_{s} u_s y_{s-1}}{\sum\limits_{s} y_{s-1}^2} \tag{3-4}$$

We write the above fraction N/D. We shall see that the bias N/D varies with the true value of γ, the size of the sample, and the size of the initial value Y. For instance, in small samples it is almost 25 per cent; in samples of 20 observations, it is about 10 per cent of the true value of γ. It never disappears, no matter what value true γ may have or how large a sample one takes.

By applying (3-2) repeatedly and letting P, Q, and R stand for polynomials, we get

$$N = (u_1 + \gamma u_2 + \gamma^2 u_3 + \cdots + \gamma^{S-1} u_S)Y + P(u_1, \ldots, u_S)$$
$$D = (1 + \gamma^2 + \gamma^4 + \cdots + \gamma^{2(S-1)})Y^2 + YQ(\gamma, u_1, \ldots, u_{S-1})$$
$$+ R(u_1, \ldots, u_{S-1})$$

By considering N/D, one can establish that the bias is aggravated the further γ is from $+1$ or -1 and the smaller the sample. Bias exists even when $\gamma = \pm 1$ or when $\gamma = 0$; the latter is truly remarkable, since the model is then reduced to $y(t) = u(t)$. Since N is a linear function of Y and the always positive denominator D is a quadratic function of Y, the bias N/D can be quite large for certain ranges of Y.

The above results generalize to model (3-1), although it is not easy to say whether the bias is up or down.

3.6. The nature of initial conditions

The following fantastically artificial example illustrates the concept of conjugate samples and what it means for initial conditions $y(0)$ to be random or fixed.

An outfit that runs automatic cafeterias has its customers use, instead of coins, special tokens made of copper. The company has several cafeterias across the country, but its customers rarely think of taking their leftover tokens with them when they travel or move from city to city. As there is at most one cafeteria per city, each cafeteria's tokens are like independent, closed monetary systems. Let us look at a single cafeteria of this kind.

Originally it had coined a number of brand-new tokens and put them in circulation, using $y(0)$ pounds of copper. Thereafter, the amount of copper in the tokens is subject to two influences. (1) To begin with, the tokens wear out as they are used. The velocity of token circulation is equal in all cities, and customers' pockets, hands, keys, and other objects that rub against the tokens are equally abrasive in all cities. Thus, in each city, year t inherits only a part γ $(0 \leq \gamma < 1)$ of the copper circulating in the previous year. (2) In addition to the systematic factor of wear and tear, random influences are at play. First, some customer's child now and then swallows a token; this disappears utterly from circulation into the city's sewers. However, occasionally there is an opposite tendency. An amateur but successful counterfeiter mints his own token now and then, or a lost token is found inside a fish and put back into circulation. So the copper remaining in circulation is described by the stochastic model (3-2). The problem for the company is how to estimate the true survival rate of its tokens.

It is very important to interpret correctly our first assumption that "$u(t)$ is a random variable in each time period t." It means that $u(t)$ is capable of assuming at least two values (opposites, if u is symmetrical) in the same period of time. But how can it? Here we need a concept of *conjugate cities* analogous to *conjugate samples*. Imagine that the only positive disturbances come from one counterfeiter and that the only negative disturbances come from one child, the counterfeiter's child, who swallows tokens. The counterfeiter is divorced, the child was awarded to the mother, and the two parents always live in separate cities, say, Ames and Buffalo; but who lives where in year t is decided at random. Ames and Buffalo are conjugate cities, because, when one experiences counterfeiting, $+u(t)$, the other necessarily experiences swallowing, $-u(t)$. If there were more families like this one, the set of conjugate cities would have to expand enough to accommodate all permutations of the various values that $\pm u(t)$ is capable of assuming.

We have *fixed initial conditions* if each cafeteria starts with the same poundage, and *random initial conditions* when the initial poundage is a random variable. To estimate the token survival rate, different procedures should be used in the two cases.

3.7. Unbiased estimation

Unbiased estimation of γ is possible only if the initial copper endowment is a fixed constant Y. The only unbiased estimate is given by the ratio of the first two successive y's using data from a single city:

$$\tilde{\gamma} = \frac{y(1)}{y(0)} = \frac{y(1)}{Y} \tag{3-5}$$

which is a degenerate least squares estimate.

This result is really startling. It says that we must throw out any information we may have about copper supply anywhere, except in year 0 and year 1 in, say, Ames. Unless we do this we can never hope to get an unbiased estimate. Estimating γ without bias when each city starts with a different amount of copper is an impossible task. A complete census of copper in *all cities* (i) in two successive years would give the correct (not just unbiased) estimate

$$\tilde{\gamma} = \frac{\sum_i y_i(t)}{\sum_i y_i(t-1)} = \gamma + \frac{\varepsilon[u(t)]}{\sum_i y_i(t-1)} = \gamma$$

We can draw another fascinating conclusion: If we have the bad luck to start off with different endowments, we can never get an unbiased estimate of γ. But suppose we find that the endowments of *all* cities happen to be equal later, say, in period $t - 1$. Then all we have to do is wait for the next year, measure the copper of any one city, say, Buffalo, and compute the ratio

$$\tilde{\gamma} = \frac{y_t}{y_{t-1}} \tag{3-6}$$

which is an unbiased estimate. (Where the information would come from, that all cities have an equal token supply in year $t - 1$, is another matter.)

The experimental scientist is, however, free from such predicaments. If he thinks radium decays as in (3-2), then he can *make* initial conditions equal by putting aside in several boxes equal lumps of radium. Then he can let them decay for a year, remeasure them, apply (3-6) to the contents of any one box, and average the results. Any one box gives an unbiased estimate. Averaging the contents of several boxes gives an estimate that is efficient as well as unbiased.

The econometrician cannot control his initial conditions in this way. If he wants an unbiased estimate, he must throw away, as prescribed, most of his information, use formula (3-6), and thus get an unbiased and inefficient estimate. Or else he may decide that he wants to reduce the variance of the estimate at the cost of introducing some bias; then he will use a formula like that of Exercise 3.C below or some more complicated version of it.

Autoregressive equations are related to the *moving average*, a technique commonly employed to interpolate data, to estimate trends, and to isolate cyclical components of time series. The statistical pitfalls of estimating (3-2) plague time series analysis, and they are not the only pitfalls. The last chapter of this book returns to some of these problems.

Exercises

3.A Prove that (3-5) is unbiased.

3.B Prove that $\bar{\gamma} = y(2)/y(1)$ is biased.

3.C Prove that $\bar{\gamma} = [y(2) + y(1)]/[y(1) + Y]$ is biased.

3.D Let u_t in (3-2) have the symmetrical distribution $q(u_t)$ with finite variance. "Symmetrical" means $q(u_t) = q(-u_t)$. Then the likelihood function of a random consecutive sample is $\prod_{s=1}^{S} q(u_s)$. Prove that the maximum likelihood estimate of γ is obtained by minimizing the expression $\sum_s \log q(\hat{u}_s)$, where the $\hat{u}_s$ are the vertical deviations from the line that we are seeking.

3.E By the method of conjugate samples or by any other method, prove or disprove the conjecture that the estimate of Exercise 3.D is biased.

Further readings

The reader who wants to see for himself how intricate is the statistical theory of even the simplest possible lagged model (3-2) may look up "Least-Squares Bias in Time Series," by Leonid Hurwicz, chap. 15 of KOOPMANS, pp. 365–383. TINTNER, pp. 255–260, gives examples and shows additional complications.

CHAPTER 4

Pitfalls of simultaneous interdependence

4.1. Simultaneous interdependence

"Everything depends on everything else" is the theme song of the Economic and the Celestial Spheres. It means that several contemporaneous endogenous variables hang from one another by means of several *distinct* causal strings. Thus, there are *two causal* (more politely, *functional*) *relations* between aggregate consumption and aggregate income: Since people are one another's customers, consumption causes income, and, since people work to eat, income causes consumption. The two relationships are, respectively, the national income identity in its simplest form

$$y_t = c_t \tag{4-1}$$

and the (unlagged) stochastic consumption function in its simplest form

$$c_t = \alpha + \beta y_t + u_t \tag{4-2}$$

We can imagine that causal forces flow from the right to the left of the two equality signs.

The moral of this chapter is that, if endogenous variables, like c and y, are connected in several ways, like (4-1) and (4-2), every statistical procedure that ignores even one of the ways is bound to be wrong. The statistical procedure must reflect the economic interdependence.

4.2. Exogenous variables

I shall not vouch for the Heavens, but in economics there are such things as *exogenous variables*. A variable exogenous to the economic sphere is a variable, like an earthquake, that influences some economic variables, like rents and food prices, without being influenced back. The random term u is, ideally, exogenous—though in practice it is a catchall for *all unknown or unspecified influences*, exogenous or endogenous. One thing is certain: Earthquakes and such are not influenced by disturbances in consumption. Indeed, the definition of an exogenous variable is that it has no connection with the random component of an economic relationship.

My prototype exogenous variable, investment z, is not really exogenous to the economic system, especially in the long run, but we shall bow to tradition and convenience for the sake of exposition.

4.3. Haavelmo's proposition

The models in this chapter, like the single-equation models treated so far, (1) are linear and (2) have all the Simplifying Properties. Therefore, they are subject to all the pitfalls I have pointed out so far. Unlike the models of Chaps. 1 to 3, the new models each contain at least two equations. Most of my examples will have precisely two (and not three or four) for convenience only, since the results can easily be extended.

New kinds of complication arise when a second equation is added.

1. *The identification problem*

It is sometimes impossible to estimate the parameters—this problem is side-stepped until Chap. 6.

2. *The Haavelmo[1] problem*

The intuitively obvious way of estimating the parameters of a two-equation model is wrong, even in the simplest of cases, where one of the equations is an identity.   We shall see that pedestrian methods are unable to estimate correctly the marginal propensity to consume out of current income, no matter how many years of income and consumption data we may have.   Even infinite samples overestimate the marginal propensity to consume.   This difficulty is as strategic as it sounds incredible.   It means that the multiplier gets overestimated and, hence, that counterdepression policies will undershoot full employment and counterinflation policies will be too timid.   Because of bad statistical procedures, the cure of unemployment or inflation comes too slowly.

The model is as follows:

$$c_t = \alpha + \beta y_t + u_t \qquad \text{(consumption function)} \quad (4\text{-}2)$$
$$c_t + z_t = y_t \qquad \text{(income identity)} \qquad (4\text{-}3)$$

where z_t (investment) is exogenous, and u_t has all the Simplifying Properties.[2]   We shall illustrate by assuming the convenient values $\alpha = 5$, $\beta = 0.5$.

In Fig. 7, line FG represents the true relation $c_t = 5 + 0.5y_t$.   When the random disturbance is positive, the line moves up; with negative disturbance, it moves down.   Lines HJ and KL correspond, respectively, to random errors equal to $+2$ and -2. OQ, the 45° line through the origin, represents equation (4-3) for the special case in which investment z is zero.   In the years when investment is zero, the only combinations of income and consumption we could possibly observe will have to lie on OQ, because nowhere else can there be equilibrium.   If, for instance, in years 1900 and 1917 investment had

---

[1] For reference to Haavelmo, see Further Readings at the end of this chapter.

[2] To be specific, Assumption 6 in this case requires that u and z shall not influence each other, either in the same time period or with a lag.   But the random term u cannot be independent of y.   The reason is that α and β are constants, z is fixed outside the economic sphere, and u comes, so to speak, from a table of random numbers; if this is so, then, by equations (4-2) and (4-3), α, β, z, and u *necessarily* determine y (and c).   Thus variable y is not predetermined but codetermined with c.   These statements summarize and anticipate the remainder of the chapter.

been zero and if the errors had been $+2$ and -2, respectively, then points P and P' would have been observed.

Let us now suppose that in some years investment z_t equals 3. Line MN (also 45° steep) describes the situation, which is that $c_t + 3 = y_t$. With errors $u_t = \pm 2$, the observable points are at R and R'. With errors *ranging* from -2 to $+2$, all observable points fall *between* R and R'.

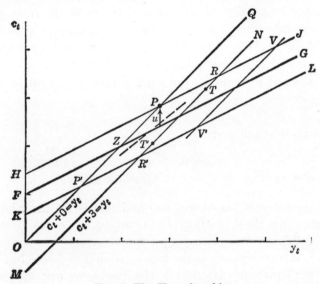

Fig. 7. The Haavelmo bias.

Let us now pass a least-squares-regression line through a scatter diagram of income and consumption, minimizing squares in the vertical sense and arguing that *from the point of view of the consumption function* income causes consumption, not vice versa. Such a procedure is bound to overestimate the slope β of the consumption function and to underestimate its intercept α. This is *Haavelmo's proposition*.

The least squares line (in dashes) corresponds to observation points that lie in the area $PP'R'R$. It is tilted counterclockwise relative to the true line FG because of the pull of "extreme" points in the corners next to R and P'. The less investment z ranges and the bigger the stochastic errors u are, the stronger is the counterclockwise pull, because lines PP' and RR' fall closer together.

This overestimating of β persists even if we allow investment to range very far. Though it is true that the parallelogram $PP'R'R$ gets longer and longer toward the northeast (say, it becomes $PVV'P'$) the fact remains that V and P', the extreme corners, help to tilt the least squares line upward. This suggests that perhaps we ought to minimize squares not in a vertical direction but in a direction running from southwest to northeast. In this particular case (though not generally) diagonal least squares are precisely correct and equivalent to the procedure of *simultaneous estimation* described in the following section.

4.4. Simultaneous estimation

We know that two relations, not one, account for the slanted position of the universe points in Fig. 7. Had the consumption function been at work alone, a given income change Δy would result in a change in consumption $\Delta c = \beta \, \Delta y$. Had the income identity been at work alone, then to the same change in income would correspond a larger change in consumption $\Delta c = \Delta y$. In fact, both relations are at work. Therefore, the total manifest response of consumption to income is neither $\Delta c = \beta \, \Delta y$ nor $\Delta c = \Delta y$, but something in between. This is why the line in dashes is steeper than FG (and less steep than OQ).

In order to isolate the β effect from a sample of points like $PP'R'R$, both relations must be allowed for. This is done by rewriting the model:

$$c_t = \frac{\alpha}{1 - \beta} + \frac{\beta}{1 - \beta} z_t + \frac{u_t}{1 - \beta} \tag{4-4}$$

$$y_t = \frac{\alpha}{1 - \beta} + \frac{1}{1 - \beta} z_t + \frac{u_t}{1 - \beta} \tag{4-5}$$

The term $u_t/(1 - \beta)$ has the same properties as u_t except that it has a different variance. Therefore the error term in the new model has all the Simplifying Properties. Either of the new equations constitutes a single-equation model with one endogenous variable (c and y, respectively) and one independent variable (z in both cases). Therefore, the estimating techniques of Sec. 2.5 can be applied to the sophisticated parameters $\alpha' = \alpha/(1 - \beta)$, $\gamma_1 = \beta/(1 - \beta)$, $\gamma_2 = 1/(1 - \beta)$. Denote these estimates by the hat ($\hat{\ }$). For the naïve least squares estimate of α and β, derived from regressing c on y, use the bird ($\check{\ }$). Let us now express these estimates in terms of moments, and let us do it for β, γ_1, and γ_2 only, leaving aside α and α'.

$$\hat{\gamma}_1 = \frac{\hat{\beta}}{1 - \hat{\beta}} = \frac{m_{cz}}{m_{zz}}$$

$$\hat{\gamma}_2 = \frac{1}{1 - \hat{\beta}} = \frac{m_{yz}}{m_{zz}}$$

$$\breve{\beta} = \frac{m_{cy}}{m_{yy}}$$

$\breve{\beta}$ is a biased estimate of β, because

$$\breve{\beta} = \frac{m_{cy}}{m_{yy}} = \frac{m_{(\alpha + \beta y + u)y}}{m_{yy}} = \beta + \frac{m_{uy}}{m_{yy}}$$

and it is known that

$$\varepsilon \frac{m_{uy}}{m_{yy}} \neq 0 \qquad\qquad (4\text{-}6)$$

$\breve{\beta}$ is inconsistent, because

$$\breve{\beta} = \frac{m_{cy}}{m_{yy}} = \frac{m_{\left(\frac{\alpha}{1-\beta} + \frac{\beta}{1-\beta}z + \frac{u}{1-\beta}\right)\left(\frac{\alpha}{1-\beta} + \frac{1}{1-\beta}z + \frac{u}{1-\beta}\right)}}{m_{\left(\frac{\alpha}{1-\beta} + \frac{1}{1-\beta}z + \frac{u}{1-\beta}\right)\left(\frac{\alpha}{1-\beta} + \frac{1}{1-\beta}z + \frac{u}{1-\beta}\right)}}$$

$$= \frac{m_{(\alpha + \beta z + u)(z + \alpha + u)}}{m_{(z + \alpha + u)(z + \alpha + u)}} = \frac{\beta + (1 + \beta)(m_{uz}/m_{zz}) + m_{uu}/m_{zz}}{1 + 2m_{uz}/m_{zz} + m_{uu}/m_{zz}}$$

The various moments m_{cy}, m_{uu}, etc., vary in value, of course, from sample to sample. As the sample size approaches the population size, however, m_{uz} approaches cov $(u,z) = 0$, m_{uu} approaches var $u > 0$, and m_{zz} approaches var $z > 0$. Therefore,

$$\text{Plim } \breve{\beta} = \frac{\beta + \text{var } u/\text{var } z}{1 + \text{var } u/\text{var } z} > \beta$$

Exercises

4.A In similar fashion prove that Plim $\breve{\alpha} < \alpha$.

4.B Interpret (4-6).

4.C Show that $1/(1 - \breve{\beta})$ is a biased estimate of $1/(1 - \beta)$. *Hint:* manipulate the expression

$$\frac{1}{1 - \breve{\beta}} = \frac{1}{1 - m_{cy}/m_{yy}}$$

and use the fact that $\varepsilon(m_{yz}/m_{zz}) = 1/(1 - \beta)$.

4.D Prove that $\hat{\gamma}_1$ is an unbiased and consistent estimate of $\beta/(1 - \beta)$.

4.E Prove that $\hat{\gamma}_2$ is an unbiased and consistent estimate of $1/(1 - \beta)$.

4.F Prove that $\hat{\gamma}_1$ and $\hat{\gamma}_2$ yield a single compatible estimate of β, which we call $\hat{\beta}$; $\hat{\beta} = m_{cz}/m_{yy}$.

4.G Prove that $\hat{\beta}$ is a biased but consistent estimate of β.

4.H From the facts that $\hat{\beta} = \beta + m_{uz}/m_{yy}$ and that $\breve{\beta} = \beta + m_{uy}/m_{yy}$, argue that the bias of $\hat{\beta}$ is less serious than the bias of $\breve{\beta}$.

Digression on directional least squares

What do we get if, in Fig. 7, we minimize the sum of the square deviations not vertically but from the southwest to the northeast? Let $P(y,c)$ in Fig. 8 stand for any point of the sample; $p = PZ$ is

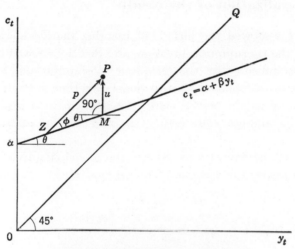

Fig. 8. Directional least squares.

parallel to the 45° line. Let θ be the angle of inclination of the true consumption function; that is, let $\tan \theta$ be the slope of the curve $\alpha + \beta y = \beta$. Then in triangle PZM, from the law of sines, we have

$$\frac{u}{\sin \phi} = \frac{p}{\sin (90 + \theta)}$$

from which it follows that

$$p_t = \frac{\sqrt{2}}{1 - \beta}\, u_t = \frac{\sqrt{2}}{1 - \beta}\, (c_t - \alpha - \beta y_t)$$

Then,

$$\sum p_s^2 = \frac{2}{(1-\beta)^2} \sum u_s^2 = \frac{2}{(1-\beta)^2} m_{(c-\alpha-\beta y)(c-\alpha-\beta y)}$$

Setting $c = y - z$,

$$\sum p_s^2 = \frac{2}{(\beta-1)^2} [m_{zz} + (\beta-1)^2 m_{yy} + 2(\beta-1)m_{yz}]$$

Minimizing Σp_s^2 with respect to $\beta - 1$, we obtain

$$\frac{1}{1-\beta} = \frac{m_{yz}}{m_{zz}}$$

that is to say, the same expression that we found for $\hat{\gamma}_2$.

4.5. Generalization of the results

Section 4.3 showed the pitfalls of ignoring the income identity in estimating the consumption function, and Sec. 4.4 showed how to get around this difficulty by the technique of simultaneous estimation, which takes into account the entire model even though the investigator may be interested in only a part. Chapters 5 to 9 deal with the intricacies of simultaneous estimation and various approximations thereof.

To prepare the way, let us enlarge the model slightly, by making investment respond to income. The new model is

$$c_t = \alpha + \beta y_t + u_t \qquad (4\text{-}2)$$
$$i_t = z_t + \gamma + \delta y_t + v_t \qquad (4\text{-}7)$$
$$c_t + i_t = y_t \qquad (4\text{-}8)$$

where z_t is autonomous investment; i_t is total investment; and u_t, v_t are random disturbances independent of each other and of present and past values of z. The last sentence is a statement of Simplifying Assumption 7, which will be explained and justified in the next chapter.

Letting $s_t = y_t - c_t$ stand for saving, we obtain from (4-2) the saving function

$$s_t = -\alpha + (1-\beta)y_t - u_t \qquad (4\text{-}9)$$

Figure 9 shows saving SS and investment II as functions of income, with zero disturbances (thick lines) and disturbed by $\pm u, \pm v$, respectively (thin lines), and with the usual (stable) relative slopes.

Naïve least squares applied to Fig. 9 underestimate the slope $1 - \beta$ of SS (as it underestimates the slope of OQ in Fig. 7) and, hence, again overestimates the marginal propensity to consume.

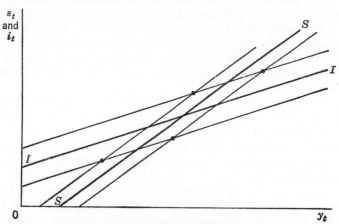

Fig. 9. The Haavelmo bias again.

4.6. Bias in the secular consumption function

We have shown that naïve curve fitting overestimates the slope of the consumption function, even with large samples and whether or not investment is a function of income. Statistical fits of the secular consumption function give a slope varying from over 0.95 to nearly 1.0, contradicting the lower figures given by budget studies, introspection, and Keynes's hunch. To reconcile these facts, consumption theories of imitation, irreversible behavior, and more and more explanatory variables have been invoked. A large part of what these ingenious theories account for can be explained by Haavelmo's proposition.

Further readings

Trygve Haavelmo's proposition was, apparently, stated first in "The Statistical Implications of a System of Simultaneous Equations" (*Econometrica*, vol. 11, no. 1, pp. 1–12, January, 1943), but a later article of his applying the proposition to the consumption function has attracted far more attention. This has appeared in three places: Trygve Haavelmo, "Methods of Measuring the Marginal Propensity to Consume" (*Journal of the American Statistical Association*, vol. 42, no. 237, pp. 105–122, March, 1947); reprinted as Cowles Commission Paper 22, new series; and again as chap. 4 of HOOD, pp. 75–91. Haavelmo gives numerical results and confidence intervals for the parameter estimates.

Jean Bronfenbrenner, "Sources and Size of Least-squares Bias in a Two-equation Model," chap. 9 of HOOD, pp. 221–235, extends Haavelmo's proposition to three more special cases. An early article by Lawrence R. Klein, "A Post-mortem on Transition Predictions of National Product" (*Journal of Political Economy*, vol. 54, no. 4, pp. 289–308, August, 1946), puts the Haavelmo proposition in proper perspective, as indicating only one of the many sources of malestimation.

Milton Friedman, *A Theory of the Consumption Function* (New York: National Bureau of Economic Research, 1957), also compares and discusses rival measurements of consumption, but his main concern is to test the Permanent Income hypothesis and to refine the consumption functions, not to discuss econometric pitfalls. It contains valuable references to the literature of the consumption function.

According to Guy H. Orcutt, "Measurement of Price Elasticities in International Trade" (*Review of Economics and Statistics*, vol. 32, no. 2, pp. 117–132, May, 1950), Haavelmo's proposition explains why exchange devaluation had been underrated as a cure to balance-of-payments difficulties. Orcutt confines mathematics to appendixes and gives many further references.

Tjalling C. Koopmans in "Statistical Estimation of Simultaneous Economic Relations" (*Journal of the American Statistical Association*, vol. 40, no. 232, pt. 1, pp. 448–466, December, 1945), discusses the Haavelmo proposition with the help of a supply-and-demand example and with interesting historical comments. When the random disturbances are viewed not as errors of observation clinging to specific variables but as errors of the econometric relationship itself, then they affect all simultaneous endogenous variables symmetrically, and Haavelmo's problem rears its head. The Koopmans article is a good preview of the next chapter.

CHAPTER 5

Many-equation linear models

5.1. Outline of the chapter

The moral of Chap. 4 is this: if a model has two equations they cannot be estimated one at a time, each without regard for the other, because both take part together in generating the phenomena from which we draw samples. This fact rules out, except in special cases, the use of the pedestrian technique of naïve least squares. Both the moral and the reasoning behind it remain in force as the number of equations in the model increases.

The present chapter is rather unimportant, and might be skipped or skimmed at first. All its principles are implicit in Chap. 4.

The main task of Chap. 5 is to systematize the study of many-equation linear models. First we present some standard and effort-saving notation (Sec. 5.2). Next, we review the Simplifying Assumptions, which were originally introduced for one-equation models in Chap. 1, to see precisely how they extend to the general case (Sec. 5.3). With two or more equations, a seventh Simplifying Assumption is required, that of *stochastic independence among the equations* (Sec. 5.4).

The presence of several simultaneous equations in a model complicates the likelihood function with the term det $\mathbf{J}$, which we have ignored until now; in intricate fashion det $\mathbf{J}$ involves the parameters of all equations in the system. (The last proposition merely restates the moral of Chap. 4.) The digression on Jacobians explains what det $\mathbf{J}$ is doing in the likelihood function.

If we heed the moral to the letter and take det $\mathbf{J}$ into account, we get into awfully long computations (see Sec. 5.5) in spite of all our original Simplifying Assumptions.

Whether computations are long or short, it pays to lay them out in an orderly way. This is a general precept, of course, but its value stands out most dramatically in the present chapter. It pays not only to do computations in an orderly manner but also to perform some redundant ones just in case you might want to check some alternative. Econometricians normally settle down to a specific model only after much experimentation. And, further, redundant computations become necessary when we want to estimate a given promising model by increasingly refined techniques. The wisdom of performing the redundant computations will become fully apparent only after we have dealt with overidentified systems, instrumental variables, limited information, and Theil's method (Chaps. 6 to 9).

5.2. Effort-saving notation

It pays to establish once and for all a uniform notation for complete linear models of several equations. These are *conventions*, not assumptions.

The endogenous variables are denoted by y's. There are G endogenous variables, called y_1, y_2, . . . , y_G and, collectively, $\mathbf{y}$. $\mathbf{y}$ is the vector $(y_1, y_2, \ldots, y_G)$. We use g ($g = 1, 2, \ldots, G$) as running subscript for endogenous variables.

The exogenous variables are denoted by z's. There are H exogenous variables, called z_1, z_2, . . . , z_H, and $\mathbf{z}$ is their vector. These may be lagged values of the y's only by special mention. The running subscript of an exogenous variable is $h = 1, 2, \ldots, H$.

All definitions have been solved out of the system, so that there are exactly G equations, all stochastic, with errors u_1, u_2, . . . , u_G. $\mathbf{u} = (u_1, u_2, \ldots, u_G)$. We speak of the gth equation.

The coefficients of the y's are called βs, and those of the z's are called

γs. They bear two subscripts: the first refers to the equation, the second to the variable to which the parameter corresponds.

We get rid of the constant term (if any) by letting the last exogenous variable z_H be identically equal to 1; its parameter γ_{gH} then becomes the constant term. In most applications we shall not bother to write the constant term at all. Either it is in the last term $\gamma_{gH}z_H = 1$, or it has been eliminated by measuring all variables from their means.

B and $\boldsymbol{\Gamma}$ represent the matrices of coefficients in their natural order:

$$
\mathbf{B} = \begin{bmatrix} \beta_{11} & \beta_{12} & \cdots & \beta_{1G} \\ \beta_{21} & \beta_{22} & \cdots & \beta_{2G} \\ \cdot & \cdot & & \cdot \\ \cdot & \cdot & & \cdot \\ \cdot & \cdot & & \cdot \\ \beta_{G1} & \beta_{G2} & \cdots & \beta_{GG} \end{bmatrix} \qquad \boldsymbol{\Gamma} = \begin{bmatrix} \gamma_{11} & \gamma_{12} & \cdots & \gamma_{1H} \\ \gamma_{21} & \gamma_{22} & \cdots & \gamma_{2H} \\ \cdot & \cdot & & \cdot \\ \cdot & \cdot & & \cdot \\ \cdot & \cdot & & \cdot \\ \gamma_{G1} & \gamma_{G2} & \cdots & \gamma_{GH} \end{bmatrix}
$$

B is always square and of size $G \times G$; $\boldsymbol{\Gamma}$ is of size $G \times H$. **A** stands for the elements of **B** and $\boldsymbol{\Gamma}$ set side by side:

$$\mathbf{A} = [\mathbf{B}\boldsymbol{\Gamma}]$$

that is to say, for the matrix of all coefficients in the model, whether they belong to endogenous or exogenous variables. **A** is of size $G \times (G + H)$.

x stands for the elements of **y** and **z** set side by side.

$$\mathbf{x} = (y_1, y_2, \ldots, y_G; z_1, z_2, \ldots, z_H)$$

that is to say, **x** is the vector of all variables, whether endogenous or exogenous, but in their natural order.

$\boldsymbol{\alpha}_1$ stands for the first row of **A**, $\boldsymbol{\alpha}_2$ for the second row, etc.; similarly, for $\boldsymbol{\beta}_1, \boldsymbol{\beta}_2, \ldots, \boldsymbol{\beta}_G, \boldsymbol{\gamma}_1, \boldsymbol{\gamma}_2, \ldots, \boldsymbol{\gamma}_G$. That is, a lower-case bold Greek letter with a single subscript g represents (some of) the parameters of a single equation (the gth) of the system.

We reduce the number of parameters to be estimated by dividing each equation by one of its coefficients. This does not affect the model in any other way. We use the gth coefficient of the gth equation for this, so that $\beta_{gg} = 1$. Henceforth we shall always take matrix $\boldsymbol{\beta}$ in its "standardized form"

$$\mathbf{B} = \begin{bmatrix} 1 & \beta_{12} & \cdots & \beta_{1G} \\ \beta_{21} & 1 & \cdots & \beta_{2G} \\ \cdot & \cdot & & \cdot \\ \cdot & \cdot & & \cdot \\ \cdot & \cdot & & \cdot \\ \beta_{G1} & \beta_{G2} & \cdots & 1 \end{bmatrix}$$

A model can be written in a variety of forms:

1. *Explicitly,* as below (time subscripts omitted):

$$y_1 + \beta_{12}y_2 + \cdots + \beta_{1G}y_G + \gamma_{11}z_1 + \gamma_{12}z_2 + \cdots + \gamma_{1H}z_H = u_1$$
$$\beta_{21}y_1 + y_2 + \cdots + \beta_{2G}y_G + \gamma_{21}z_1 + \gamma_{22}z_2 + \cdots + \gamma_{2H}z_H = u_2$$

$$\beta_{G1}y_1 + \beta_{G2}y_2 + \cdots + y_G + \gamma_{G1}z_1 + \gamma_{G2}z_2 + \cdots + \gamma_{GH}z_H = u_G$$

$$(5\text{-}1)$$

2. In *extended vector form*:

$$\boldsymbol{\beta}_1\mathbf{y} + \boldsymbol{\gamma}_1\mathbf{z} = u_1$$
$$\boldsymbol{\beta}_2\mathbf{y} + \boldsymbol{\gamma}_2\mathbf{z} = u_2$$

$$\boldsymbol{\beta}_G\mathbf{y} + \boldsymbol{\gamma}_G\mathbf{z} = u_G$$

$$(5\text{-}2)$$

3. In *condensed vector form*:

$$\boldsymbol{\alpha}_1\mathbf{x} = u_1$$
$$\boldsymbol{\alpha}_2\mathbf{x} = u_2$$

$$\boldsymbol{\alpha}_G\mathbf{x} = u_G$$

$$(5\text{-}3)$$

4. In *extended matrix form*:

$$\mathbf{By} + \boldsymbol{\Gamma}\mathbf{z} = \mathbf{u} \qquad (5\text{-}4)$$

5. In *condensed matrix form*:

$$\mathbf{Ax} = \mathbf{u} \qquad (5\text{-}5)$$

Note that, when the context is clear, bold lower-case letters stand either for a row or for a column vector.

Finally, $\sigma_{gh}(t)$ stands for the covariance of $u_g(t)$ with $u_h(t)$; $\delta_{gh}(t)$ is the matrix of these covariances; and $\delta^{gh}(t)$ is its inverse.

5.3. The Six Simplifying Assumptions generalized

A laconic mathematician can generalize the Six Simplifying Assumptions with a stroke of brevity by saying that they continue to apply if we replace the symbol u by $\mathbf{u}$.   Our task is to interpret this in terms of economics.

In Chap. 1, I discussed the Six Simplifying Properties when there was a single equation in the model and, therefore, a single disturbance. Now we have one disturbance for each equation, and $\mathbf{u}$ is the vector made up of them, $\mathbf{u}(t) = (u_1(t), u_2(t), \ldots, u_G(t))$.

Assumption 1

"$\mathbf{u}$ is a random variable" means that each $u_g(t)$ is a random variable, that is to say, that all equations remaining after solving out the definitions are stochastic.

Assumption 2

"$\mathbf{u}$ has expected value $\mathbf{0}$" means that the mean of the joint distribution is the vector $\mathbf{0} = (0, 0, \ldots, 0)$, or that each u_g has zero expected value.

Assumption 3

"$\mathbf{u}$ has constant variance" means that the covariances

$$\sigma_{gh} = \operatorname{cov}(u_g, u_h)$$

of the several disturbances do not vary with time.

Assumption 4

"$\mathbf{u}$ is normal" means that $u_1(t)$, $u_2(t)$, $\ldots$, $u_G(t)$ are jointly normally distributed.

Assumption 5

"$\mathbf{u}$ is not autocorrelated" means that there is no correlation between the disturbance of one equation and previous values of itself.

Assumption 6

"**u** is not correlated with **z**" means that no exogenous variable—in whichever equation it appears—is correlated with any disturbance, past, present, or future, of any equation in the model.

On these assumptions, the likelihood function of the sample is

$$L = (2\pi)^{-S/2}(\det \mathbf{J})^S(\det [\mathfrak{d}_{gh}])^{-S/2} \exp \left\{ - \tfrac{1}{2} \sum_{s=1}^{S} \mathbf{u}_s[\mathfrak{d}^{gh}]\mathbf{u}_s \right\} \quad (5\text{-}6)$$

which should be compared with (2-2). The analogy is perfect. The expression in the curly braces can also be written

$$- \tfrac{1}{2} \sum_s \sum_g \sum_h u_g(s)\sigma^{gh}u_h(s) \quad (5\text{-}7)$$

Another way to write the likelihood function is

$$L = (2\pi)^{-S/2}(\det \mathbf{J})^S(\det [\mathfrak{d}_{gh}])^{-S/2} \exp \left\{ -\tfrac{1}{2} \sum_s \mathbf{A}\mathbf{x}(s)[\mathfrak{d}^{gh}]\mathbf{x}(s)\mathbf{A} \right\} \quad (5\text{-}8)$$

which brings out the fact that L is a function (1) of all the unknown parameters $\beta_{gh}, \gamma_{gh}, \sigma^{gh}, \sigma_{gh}$; and (2) of all the observations $\mathbf{x}(s)$ ($s = 1, 2, \ldots, S$). The function's logarithmic form

$$S^{-1} \log L = -\tfrac{1}{2} \log 2\pi + \log \det \mathbf{J} - \tfrac{1}{2} \log \det [\mathfrak{d}_{gh}]$$
$$- \tfrac{1}{2} \sum_{s=1}^{S} \mathbf{A}\mathbf{x}(s)[\mathfrak{d}^{gh}]\mathbf{x}(s)\mathbf{A} \quad (5\text{-}9)$$

is easier to use.

5.4. Stochastic independence

The seventh Simplifying Assumption: $\mathfrak{d}_{gh}$ *is a diagonal matrix,* or

$$\mathrm{cov}\,(u_g, u_h) = 0 \quad \text{for } g \neq h$$

is not obligatory, but it is easy to rationalize. It states that *the disturbance of one equation is not correlated with the disturbance in any other equation of the model in the same time period*—something quite different from Assumption 6.

Recall that each random term is a gathering of errors of measurement, errors of aggregation, omitted variables, omitted equations, and errors of linear approximation. Assumption 7 states that either (1) the gth equation and the hth equation are disturbed by different random causes, or (2) if they are disturbed by the same causes, different "drawings" go into $u_g(t)$ and $u_h(t)$. This assumption is clearly inapplicable in the following situations:

1. In year t, all or nearly all statistics were subject to larger than the usual errors, because of a cut in the budget of the Statistics Bureau.

2. Errors of aggregation affect mainly national income (because of shifts in distribution), and national income enters several equations of the model.

3. Omitted variables (one or more) are known to affect two (or more) equations. For instance, weather affects the supply of watermelons, cotton, and whale blubber. Now if the model contains equations for watermelons and blubber, the inclusion of weather in the random term does not hurt, because relatively *independent* drawings of weather (one in the Southeast, one in the South Pacific) affect these two industries. However, if watermelons and cotton are included in the model, both of these are grown in the same belt, the weather affecting them is one and the same, and Assumption 7 is violated.

Assumption 7 simplifies the computations (1) because it leaves fewer covariances to estimate, (2) because det δ_{gh} becomes a simple product $\Pi\sigma_{gg}$, and (3) because all the cross terms[1] in (5-7) drop out. This can reduce computations by a factor of 2 or 3 for a model of as few as three equations and by a much greater factor for larger systems.

Digression on Jacobians

The likelihood function involves a term expressed as det $\mathbf{J}$, the Jacobian of the functions u, say, with respect to the variables y; we have disregarded det $\mathbf{J}$ until now, since we have taken it on faith to be equal to 1. This is no longer true in a many-equation model. Here $\mathbf{J}$ is a matrix of unknown parameters, the same βs, in fact, that we are trying to estimate with the likelihood function.

The main ideas behind $\mathbf{J}$ are three:

1. If you know the probability distribution of a variable u (or several variables $u_1, u_2, \ldots, u_G$), then you can find the proba-

---

[1] Those for which $g \neq h$.

bility distribution of a variable y related to u functionally (or of several y's related functionally to the u's).

2. If the u's and y's are equally numerous and if the functions connecting the two sets are one-to-one, continuous, and with continuous first derivatives, then the matrix $\mathbf{J}$ of all partial derivatives of the form $\partial u / \partial y$ will have an inverse.

3. If conditions 1 and 2 are satisfied, then we can calculate the joint probability distribution q of the y's from the known joint probability distribution p of the u's (omitting the subscript t) as follows:

$$p(u_1, u_2, \ldots, u_G) \, du_1 \, du_2 \cdots du_G$$
$$= \det \mathbf{J} \cdot p(u_1, u_2, \ldots, u_G) \, dy_1 \, dy_2 \cdots dy_G$$
$$\text{or} \quad q(y_1, y_2, \ldots, y_G) \, dy_1 \, dy_2 \cdots dy_G \tag{5-10}$$
$$= \det \mathbf{J} \cdot p(u_1, u_2, \ldots, u_G) \, dy_1 \, dy_2 \cdots dy_G$$

I shall illustrate these three ideas by examples.

Example 1

Let u be a single variable whose probability distribution we know to be as follows:

VALUE OF u	PROBABILITY $p(u)$
-4	0.1
-3	0.2
1	0.4
3	0.3

Let y be related functionally to u as follows:

$$y(u) = u^2 - 4u + 3 \tag{5-11}$$

As u takes on its four values, y takes on the corresponding values $y(-4) = 35$, $y(-3) = 24$, $y(1) = 0$, $y(3) = 0$. Since we know how often u is equal to -4, -3, 1, and 3, we can find how often y is equal to 35, 24, and 0.

VALUE OF y	PROBABILITY $q(y)$
35	0.1
24	0.2
0	0.7

Example 2

The same can be done with several y's and u's connected by an appropriate set of functions, for instance,

$$y_1 = -u_1 + 3u_2^2 - u_3$$
$$y_2 = e^{-u_1} + \log u_2$$

provided the probability distribution $p(u_1, u_2, u_3)$ is known.

Relation (5-11) is not one-to-one, since, for every value of y, u can have two values. Accordingly, in Example 1 the second condition is violated, and the Jacobian is undefined. The same is true for Example 2.

Whenever the functional relation between the u's and y's is one-to-one, $[\partial u / \partial y]$ and $[\partial y / \partial u]$ are single-valued and their determinants multiply up to the number 1.

Example 3

$$y(u) = 3u + \log u - 4$$

Though it is very hard to express u in terms of y, we know that, since $\partial y / \partial u = 3 + 1/u = (3u + 1)/u$, the Jacobian $\mathbf{J} = \partial u / \partial y = u/(3u + 1)$.

Example 4

$$y_1 = -u_1 + u_2$$
$$y_2 = e^{-u_1} + \log u_2 + 5 \tag{5-12}$$

Here we can compute det $\mathbf{J}$ from knowledge of

$$\det \left[\frac{\partial y}{\partial u} \right] = -\frac{1}{u_2} + e^{-u_1}$$

since it follows that det $\mathbf{J} = u_2/(u_2 e^{-u_1} - 1)$. Therefore, by (5-10), the probability distribution of the y's is

$$q(y_1, y_2) \, dy_1 \, dy_2 = \frac{u_2}{u_2 e^{-u_1} - 1} \, p(u_1, u_2) \, dy_1 \, dy_2$$

Now, what relevance does all this have to econometrics? Very simple. Let $y_1, y_2, \ldots, y_G$ be endogenous variables, and let $u_1, u_2, \ldots, u_G$ be the random errors attached to the structural equations. The model's G equations are explicit functional relations between the y's and the u's, like (5-12). Directly, we know nothing at all about the probability of this or that combination of y's. Nevertheless, (5-10) allows us to compute this probability, namely, in terms of $\mathbf{J}$ and the probability distribution of the u's. It turns out that the right-hand side of (5-10) involves *only* the parameters we seek, the observations we can make, and the probability distribution p, which we have already specified when we constructed the model.

If the structural equations are all linear, as in (5-1), the matrix $\mathbf{J}$ of all partial derivatives of the form $\partial u/\partial y$ turns out to be nothing but the matrix $\mathbf{B}$ itself.

$$\mathbf{J} = \begin{bmatrix} 1 & \beta_{12} & \cdots & \beta_{1G} \\ \beta_{21} & 1 & \cdots & \beta_{2G} \\ \cdot & \cdot & & \cdot \\ \cdot & \cdot & & \cdot \\ \cdot & \cdot & & \cdot \\ \beta_{G1} & \beta_{G2} & \cdots & 1 \end{bmatrix} = \mathbf{B}$$

5.5. Interdependence of the estimates

Now that we know that $\mathbf{J} = \mathbf{B}$, we can *both* find the values β, γ, σ that maximize the likelihood function (5-9) *and* compute its actual value. Actually we do not care how large L itself is.

Naturally, maximizing such a function by ordinary methods is a staggering job; we won't undertake it. In fact, nobody undertakes it by direct attack. We shall use (5-9) to answer the following question: In order to estimate this particular parameter or this particular equation, do we need to estimate all parameters? The answer, generally, is yes.

Note first of all that the maximum likelihood method of estimating $\mathbf{B}$, $\mathbf{\Gamma}$, and σ_{gh} differs from the naïve least squares method quite radically, because the least squares method does not involve the term log det $\mathbf{B}$ at all. In other words, the least squares method, if applied to the model one equation at a time, omits from account the matrix $\mathbf{B}$; it does not allow the parameters of one equation to influence the estimation of the parameters of another; nor does it allow the covariances σ_{gh}

to influence in the least the parameter estimates of any equation that is being fitted.

Finally, the least squares technique estimates the covariances σ_{gg} one at a time without involving any other covariance. Contrariwise, in maximum likelihood, the estimates $\hat{\beta}$ of one equation affect the $\hat{\beta}$s and $\hat{\gamma}$s of another; the $\hat{\sigma}$s of one equation affect the $\hat{\beta}$s and $\hat{\gamma}$s of another; and one $\hat{\sigma}$ affects another.

In a word, the sophisticated maximum likelihood method is very expensive from the point of view of computations and is probably more refined than the quality of the raw statistical data warrants. Econometric theory is like an exquisitely balanced French recipe, spelling out precisely with how many turns to mix the sauce, how many carats of spice to add, and for how many milliseconds to bake the mixture at exactly 474 degrees of temperature. But when the statistical cook turns to raw materials, he finds that hearts of cactus fruit are unavailable, so he substitutes chunks of cantaloupe; where the recipe calls for vermicelli he uses shredded wheat; and he substitutes green garment dye for curry, ping-pong balls for turtle's eggs, and, for Chalifougnac vintage 1883, a can of turpentine.

Two courses of action are open to the econometrician who is reluctant to lavish refined computations on crude data:

1. Use the refined maximum likelihood method, but reduce the burden of computation by making additional Simplifying Assumptions.

2. Water down the maximum likelihood method to something more pedestrian but not quite so naïve as least squares. *Limited information, instrumental variable*, and other techniques are available; they are the subject of Chaps. 7, 8, and 9.

5.6. Recursive models

If **B** is a triangular matrix,[1] the model is called *recursive;* and its computation is lightened, because there are fewer βs to estimate and because det **B** $= 1$.

The economic interpretation of a recursive model is the following. There is an economic variable in the system (say, the price of coffee beans) that is affected only by exogenous variables (like Brazilian weather); next, there is a second economic variable (say, the price of a

[1] **B** is triangular if $\beta_{gh} = 0$ for all $g < h$.

cup of coffee) that is affected by exogenous variables (tax on coffee beans) and by the one endogenous variable (price of coffee beans) just mentioned. Next, there is a third economic variable (say, the number of hours spent by employees for coffee breaks) that depends only on exogenous variables (the amount of incoming gossip) and (one or both of) the first two endogenous variables but no others; and so on.

Exercises

5.A   In the recursive system

$$y_1 = \gamma z_1 + u$$
$$y_2 = \beta y_1 + \gamma_1 z_1 + \gamma_2 z_2 + v$$

let the Simplifying Properties hold for u, v with respect to the exogenous variables. Prove that, if β is estimated by naïve least squares, that is, if

$$\check{\beta} = \frac{m_{(y_2, z_1, z_2)(y_1, z_1, z_2)}}{m_{(y_1, z_1, z_2)(y_1, z_1, z_2)}}$$

then $\check{\beta}$ is biased.

5.B   In the recursive model

$$x_t = \beta y_t + u_t$$
$$y_t = \gamma x_{t-1} + v_t$$

show that $\check{\beta}$ and $\check{\gamma}$ are unbiased but that least squares applied to the autoregressive equation obtained as a combination of the two equations gives biased estimates.

Further readings

The notation of Sec. 5.2 is worth learning because it is becoming standard among econometricians. It is expanded in KOOPMANS, chap. 2.

Jacobians are illustrated by KLEIN, pp. 32–38. The mathematics of Jacobians, with proofs, can be found in Richard Courant, *Differential and Integral Calculus*, vol. 2, chap. 3 (New York: 1953), or in Wilfred Kaplan, *Advanced Calculus*, pp. 90–100 (Reading, Massachusetts: 1952).

KLEIN, p. 81, gives a simple example of a recursive model.

CHAPTER 6

Identification

6.1. Introduction

Identification problems spring up almost everywhere in econometrics as soon as one departs from single-equation models.   This chapter far from exhausts the subject.   In particular, the next two topics, instrumental variables in Chap. 7 and limited information in Chap. 8, are intimately bound up with it.   The identification problem will arise sporadically in later chapters.

Though this chapter is self-contained, some familiarity with the subject is desirable.   I know of no better elementary treatment than that of Tjalling C. Koopmans, "Identification Problems in Economic Model Construction," chap. 2 in Hood.   I have chosen to devote this chapter to a few topics which, in my opinion, either have not received convincing treatment or have not been put in pedagogic form.

The main results of this chapter are the following:

1. There are several definitions of identifiability.   I show their equivalence.

2. Lack or presence of identification may be due (*a*) to the model's *a priori* specification, (*b*) to the actual values of its unknown parameters, or (*c*) to the particular sample we happen to have drawn.

3. There are ways to detect overidentification and underidentification. These ways are not always foolproof. There are several ways to remove over- or underidentification.

4. In spite of the superficial fact that they are defined in analogous terms, *underidentification* and *overidentification* are qualitatively different properties: the former is nonstochastic, the latter stochastic; the former can be removed (in special cases) by means of additional restrictions, the latter is handled by better observations or longer computation.

6.2. Completeness and nonsingularity

The following discussion applies to all kinds of models, linear or not, large or small, but it will be illustrated by this example:

$$
\begin{aligned}
y_1 \phantom{{}+{}} & & + \gamma_{11}z_1 + \gamma_{12}z_2 + \gamma_{13}z_3 + \gamma_{14}z_4 &= u_1 \\
\beta_{21}y_1 + y_2 + \beta_{23}y_3 & + \gamma_{21}z_1 + \gamma_{22}z_2 + \gamma_{23}z_3 & &= u_2 \quad (6\text{-}1) \\
\beta_{31}y_1 \phantom{{}+{}} + y_3 & + \gamma_{31}z_1 + \gamma_{32}z_2 & &= u_3
\end{aligned}
$$

This model describes an economic mechanism that works somewhat like this:

1. The parameters β and γ are fixed constants.

2. In each time period, someone supplies outside information about the exogenous variables z.

3. In each time period, someone goes to a preassigned table of random numbers, and, using a prescribed procedure, reads off some numbers u_1, u_2, u_3.

4. All this is fed into (6-1).

5. Values for the endogenous variables, y_1, y_2, y_3, are generated in accordance with the resulting system.

The last step succeeds if and only if the linear equations resulting from step 4 are independent. Otherwise there is an infinity of compatible triplets (y_1, y_2, y_3). The model is *complete* if it can be solved uniquely for (y_1, y_2, y_3); otherwise it is incomplete. To generate a unique triplet it is necessary and sufficient that the matrix **B** be *nonsingular*, meaning that no row of it is a linear combination of other rows.

The economic interpretation of singularity and nonsingularity is very simple. Each equation in (6-1) represents the behavior of a *sector* of the economy, say, producers, consumers, bankers, buyers, sellers, or middlemen. These sectors respond to exogenous stimuli z and economic stimuli y. They may respond to exogenous stimuli in any way whatsoever. In particular, it is quite permissible for them to respond in the same way to all exogenous stimuli ($\gamma_{11} = \gamma_{21} = \gamma_{31}$, $\gamma_{12} = \gamma_{22} = \gamma_{32}$, etc.). But, if the matrix is to be nonsingular, they should respond *in different ways* to the *endogenous* stimuli. No sector may have the same β parameters as another; no sector's responses may be the average of two other sectors' responses. No sector may be a weighted average of any other sectors, as far as economic stimuli are concerned.

To illustrate singularity, consider a simple economy which consists of three families responding to three economic stimuli but such that the third family makes an average response. Then **B** is singular, and the model containing the three families is incomplete. For nonsingularity the sectors must be sufficiently unlike each other. In fact this is the definition of sectors: that they are *economically* different from one another.

Exercise

6.A Prove the following theorems by using the common sense of the five steps of the above discussion: "If Assumption 7 is made, then **B** is nonsingular," and "If **B** is singular, Assumption 7 cannot hold." These two statements can be reworded: "An econometric model is complete if and only if its sectors are stochastically independent." Appendix E proves this mathematically, but what is wanted in this exercise is an "economic" proof.

6.3. The reduced form

Every complete linear model $\mathbf{By} + \boldsymbol{\Gamma}\mathbf{z} = \mathbf{u}$ can be reduced to $\mathbf{y} = \boldsymbol{\Pi}\mathbf{z} + \mathbf{v}$. These two expressions are called *the original form* and *the reduced form*. If it is complete, the original model (6-1) can be reduced to

$$y_1 = \pi_{11}z_1 + \pi_{12}z_2 + \pi_{13}z_3 + \pi_{14}z_4 + v_1$$
$$y_2 = \pi_{21}z_1 + \pi_{22}z_2 + \pi_{23}z_3 + \pi_{24}z_4 + v_2 \qquad (6\text{-}2)$$
$$y_3 = \pi_{31}z_1 + \pi_{32}z_2 + \pi_{33}z_3 + \pi_{34}z_4 + v_3$$

Some obvious properties of (6-2) are worth pointing out: Its random disturbances v_1, v_2, v_3 are linear combinations of the original random disturbances and share their properties. However, the v's have different covariances from the u's. In particular, the v's are interdependent even if the u's were stochastically independent. (We seldom have to worry about the precise relation among the u's and v's.) Unlike the typical original form, each equation of the reduced form contains *all* the exogenous variables of the model.

Each equation of the reduced form constitutes a model that satisfies the Six Simplifying Assumptions of Chap. 1 and, therefore, may validly be estimated by least squares; these estimates are called $\tilde{\pi}$s. If it is possible to work back from the $\tilde{\pi}$s to estimate unambiguously the coefficients β, γ of the original form, we shall call such estimates $\hat{\beta}$, $\hat{\gamma}$ and say that (6-1) is *exactly identified*. Finally, the coefficients of the two forms (6-1), (6-2) are connected as follows:

$$\begin{array}{llll}
-\gamma_{11} = \pi_{11} & -\gamma_{21} = \beta_{21}\pi_{11} + \pi_{21} + \beta_{23}\pi_{31} & \gamma_{31} = \beta_{31}\pi_{11} + \pi_{31} \\
-\gamma_{12} = \pi_{12} & -\gamma_{22} = \beta_{21}\pi_{12} + \pi_{22} + \beta_{23}\pi_{32} & \gamma_{32} = \beta_{31}\pi_{12} + \pi_{32} \\
-\gamma_{13} = \pi_{13} & -\gamma_{23} = \beta_{21}\pi_{13} + \pi_{23} + \beta_{23}\pi_{33} & 0 = \beta_{31}\pi_{13} + \pi_{33} \\
-\gamma_{14} = \pi_{14} & 0 = \beta_{21}\pi_{14} + \pi_{24} + \beta_{23}\pi_{34} & 0 = \beta_{31}\pi_{14} + \pi_{34}
\end{array}$$

$$(6\text{-}3)$$

It is possible, but messy, to solve for π_{11}, . . . , π_{34} in terms of the βs and γs. The important fact is that, in general, *all* πs are *a priori* nonzero in the reduced form, even if many of the βs and γs are *a priori* zero in the original form.

Relations (6-3) can be written much more compactly:

$$-\Gamma = B\Pi \qquad\qquad (6\text{-}4)$$

6.4. Over- and underdeterminacy

As a preview for the rest of this chapter, imagine that (6-1) is complete. If so, its reduced form (6-2) exists and can be estimated by least squares. Let the estimates be $\tilde{\pi}_{11}$, . . . , $\tilde{\pi}_{34}$.

Now consider the leftmost column of equations in (6-3). Evidently the γs can be computed right away from the πs, uniquely and unambiguously. We say, then, that γ_{11}, γ_{12}, γ_{13}, γ_{14} are *exactly identified*.

Consider next the last two equations of (6-3); they give rise to two estimates of β_{31}, namely, $-\check{\pi}_{33}/\check{\pi}_{13}$ and $-\check{\pi}_{34}/\check{\pi}_{14}$, which in general are quite different, no matter how ideal the sample. When this happens to parameters, we say that they are (or the equation that contains them is) *overidentified;* accordingly, system (6-3) *overdetermines* β_{31}.

Consider now the middle column of (6-3). Its four equations *underdetermine* the five unknowns β_{21}, β_{23}, γ_{21}, γ_{22}, γ_{23}. An equation to which such parameters belong is *underidentified.*

Obviously, then, the identification problem has something to do with the number of equations and unknowns in the system $-\boldsymbol{\Gamma} = \mathbf{B\Pi}$. The Counting Rules of Sec. 6.7 will show this more precisely.

6.5. Bogus structural equations

Consider the supply-demand model

$$
\begin{array}{lll}
SS\ \text{(Supply)} & y_1 + \beta_{12}y_2 = u_1 & \\
DD\ \text{(Demand)} & \beta_{21}y_1 + y_2 = u_2 & (6\text{-}5)
\end{array}
$$

where y_1 represents price and y_2 represents quantity; linear combinations of the true supply and demand are called *bogus relations* and are branded with the superscript $\oplus$. A bogus relation may parade either as supply or as demand,

$$
SS^{\oplus} = j(SS) + k(DD) \qquad DD^{\oplus} = m(SS) + n(DD)
$$

where j, k, m, n are unknown numbers, but suitable to make the standardized coefficients $\beta_{11}^{\oplus}$, $\beta_{22}^{\oplus}$ of the bogus relations equal to 1.

The bogus coefficients are connected with the true coefficients as follows:

$$
\begin{array}{ll}
\beta_{11}^{\oplus} = j + k\beta_{21} = 1 & \beta_{12}^{\oplus} = j\beta_{12} + k \\
\beta_{21}^{\oplus} = m + n\beta_{21} & \beta_{22}^{\oplus} = m\beta_{12} + n = 1
\end{array}
$$

The bogus supply contains a random term

$$
u_1^{\oplus} = ju_1 + ku_2
$$

and the bogus demand contains an analogous term

$$
u_2^{\oplus} = mu_1 + nu_2
$$

Later on we shall use the following relations between the covariances of the bogus and the true disturbances:

$$\text{var } u_1^{\oplus} = j^2 \text{ var } u_1 + \qquad 2jk \text{ cov } (u_1,u_2) + k^2 \text{ var } u_2$$
$$\text{var } u_2^{\oplus} = m^2 \text{ var } u_1 + \qquad 2mn \text{ cov } (u_1,u_2) + n^2 \text{ var } u_2 \qquad (6\text{-}6)$$
$$\text{cov } (u_1^{\oplus},u_2^{\oplus}) = jm \text{ var } u_1 + (jn + mk) \text{ cov } (u_1,u_2) + kn \text{ var } u_2$$

6.6. Three definitions of exact identification

The discussion that follows is meant to apply to linear models only. Some results can be extended to other types of models (but not in this work).

A model or an equation in it may be either (*exactly*) *identified*, or *underidentified*, or *overidentified*. Setting aside for the moment the last two cases, here are three alternative definitions of exact identification, one in terms of the statistical appearance of the model, one in terms of maxima of the likelihood function L, and one in terms of the probability distribution of the endogenous variables.

Definition 1. A model is identified if its structural equations "look different" from the statistical point of view. An equation looks different if linear combinations of the other equations in the system cannot produce an equation involving *exactly the same variables* as the equation in question.

Thus the supply-demand model (6-5) is not exactly identified, because both equations contain the same variables, price and quantity.

In the model

$$\begin{array}{llll} SS & \quad y_1 + \beta_{12}y_2 + \gamma_{11}z_1 = u_1 \\ DD & \quad \beta_{21}y_1 + \quad y_2 \qquad \quad = u_2 \end{array} \qquad (6\text{-}7)$$

where z_1 represents rainfall, a linear combination of SS and DD contains the same variables as SS itself. Not so for DD, because every nontrivial linear combination introduces rainfall into the demand equation. In this model the demand equation is identified, but the supply is not exactly identified. In such cases the *model* is *not* exactly identified.

Definition 2. A model is identified if the likelihood function $L(S)$ has a *unique* maximum at a "point" $\mathbf{A} = \mathbf{A}^0$. This means that, if you substitute the values α^0 in L, L is maximal; at any other point L is definitely smaller. Similarly, an equation is exactly identified if the likelihood function L becomes smaller when you replace the set α_g^0 of *that* equation's parameters by any other set of α_a^1.   This way of looking at the matter is presented in detail later on, in Sec. 6.12.

Definition 3.   Anything (a model, an equation, a parameter) is called exactly identified if it can be determined from knowledge of the conditional distribution of the endogenous variables, given the exogenous.   This is to say, it is identified if, given a sample that was large enough and rich enough, you could determine the parameters in question.   We know that, no matter how large the sample or how rich, we could never disentangle the two equations of (6-5).

All three definitions appear to say that exact identification is not a stochastic property, for it does not seem to depend on the samples we may chance to draw.   We shall return to this question later on.

One must be very accurate and careful about the terminology. *Over-*, *under-*, and *exact identification* are exhaustive and mutually exclusive cases.   *Identified* means "either exactly or overidentified." *Not identified* means "underidentified."

Underidentification occurs when:

By linear combinations of the equations one can obtain a bogus equation that looks statistically like some true equation (Definition 1).

The likelihood function has a *maximum maximorum* at two or more points of the parameter space (Definition 2).

Knowledge of the conditional distribution of the endogenous variables, given the exogenous, does not determine all the parameters of the model (Definition 3).

There are three principal ways to avert (or at least to detect) absence of exact identification: (1) constraints on the *a priori* values of the parameters; (2) constraints on the estimates of the parameters; (3) constraints on the stochastic assumptions of the model.

6.7. A priori constraints on the parameters

Two new symbols will speed up the discussion considerably.   Suppose we are discussing the third equation of a model.   A single asterisk will denote the variables *present* in the third equation, a double asterisk, those *absent* from the third equation.   Asterisks can be attached to variables, to their parameters, or to vectors of such variables and parameters. The asterisk notation has now become standard in econometric literature, and Appendix F gives a detailed account of it.

The commonest *a priori* restrictions on **A** are (1) zero restrictions, like $\gamma_{24} = 0$; (2) parameter equalities in the same equation, for example, $\gamma_{21} = \gamma_{22}$; (3) other equations involving parameters of several equations *a priori*.

These cases have economic counterparts, which I proceed to illustrate.

Zero restrictions

Zero restrictions are common and handy. A zero restriction says that, for all we know, such and such a variable is irrelevant to the behavior of a given sector. If nothing but zero restrictions are contemplated, then we have a handy counting rule (Counting Rule 1) for telling whether an equation is identified.

If an equation of a model contains all the variables of the model, it is underidentified, because linear combinations of all the equations look statistically just like it. To avoid this underidentification, the following two conditions are necessary:

1. That some variables (call them x^{**}) be absent from this equation.
2. That the variables (call them x^*) present in the equation in question, whenever they appear in another equation, be mixed with at least one x^{**}.

In (6-1) the first equation is identified, because any intermixture of the second equation brings in variables y_2^{**} and y_3^{**} (double-starred from the point of view of the first equation), and intermixture of the third equation brings in y_3^{**}, which is absent from the first equation. In (6-1) the second equation is underidentified, because the third equation can be merged into it without bringing in any variable that is not already in the pure, uncontaminated second equation. Finally, the third equation is identified, because an intermixture of the first equation introduces z_3^{**} and z_4^{**}, and intermixture of the second equation introduces y_2^{**} and z_3^{**} (the double stars are now from the point of view of the third equation).

This example shows that underidentification can be detected by checking whether given strategic parameters in the model are specified *a priori* to be zero or nonzero. This justifies the following statement:

Counting Rule 1. For an equation to be exactly identified it is necessary (but not sufficient) that the number of variables absent from it be one less than the number of sectors.

Thus, if G_g^* and H_g^* are, respectively, the number of endogenous and exogenous variables present in the gth equation, then for the gth equation to be identified it is necessary (but not sufficient) that $G + H - (G_g^* + H_g^*) = G - 1$, or that $H - H_g^* = G_g^* - 1$.

Parameter equalities in the same equation

Another quite common *a priori* restriction is to set two or more parameters of a given equation *a priori* equal. For instance, let us interpret (6-1) as a model of bank behavior, where z_1 represents balances of banks at the Federal Reserve and z_2 represents balances of banks at other banks. It is conceivable that a commercial bank may conduct its loan policy by looking at its total balances and not at whether they are held at the Federal Reserve or at another bank. The restriction would be expressed $\gamma_{21} = \gamma_{22}$. On the other hand, some other sector, say, foreign banks, may treat the two kinds of balances differently, $\gamma_{32} \neq \gamma_{31}$. Under these conditions, if the third equation is intermixed with the second equation, the result cannot masquerade as the second equation, because the bogus second equation would have different coefficients for z_1 and z_2, contrary to the *a priori* assumption that the response to all balances (Federal Reserve and other) is identical.

Linear equations connecting the parameters of different equations

Suppose that a model contains a production function and an equation showing the distribution of national income by factor shares. Then the coefficient of the share of labor is *a priori* equal to the labor coefficient of the production function, on the grounds of the marginal productivity theory of wages.

Collectively, all the *linear* restrictions on **A** discussed so far can be capsuled into *Counting Rule* 2. Let $\mathbf{A}_g^{**}$ be what is left of **A** if we throw out the columns corresponding to the variables present in the gth equation.

Counting Rule 2. For the gth equation to be exactly identified it is necessary and sufficient that the matrix $\mathbf{A}_g^{**}$ have rank $G - 1$.

These tests and counting rules can (and should) be applied before you start computations.

There are no convenient counting rules for nonlinear restrictions on the parameters.

Inequalities such as $\alpha > 0$ or $\alpha \geq 0$ do not help to remove under-identification. For instance, knowledge that demand is downward-sloping and that supply is upward-sloping does not help to identify the model (6-5).

6.8. Constraints on parameter estimates

Consider again the supply-demand model (6-7). It states *a priori* that rainfall influences supply and not demand; and this restriction identifies the demand equation (but not the supply). Now imagine that you draw an unlucky sample made up of cases where the other random elements u_1 have annihilated the theoretical effect of rainfall. You will get $\tilde{\gamma}_{11}$ (for *this* sample) equal to zero. The *sample* has behaved as if rainfall did not influence supply, i.e., as if the model were reduced to (6-5), where the demand was statistically indistinguishable from the supply.

The moral of this is: If you are not *a priori* certain that supply is influenced by rainfall (not only theoretically but also in the sample period) then do not proceed with the estimation of demand. If you fear that rainfall fails to affect supply (whether in the sample or generally), then to estimate the demand introduce in the supply function another variable z_2 (say, last year's price of a competing crop) that you are *certain* influences (if ever so little) this year's supply both theoretically and in the sample period. The new model then is

$$
\begin{aligned}
SS \qquad & y_1 + \beta_{12}y_2 + \gamma_{11}z_1 + \gamma_{12}z_2 = u_1 \\
DD \qquad & \beta_{21}y_1 + \quad y_2 \qquad\qquad\qquad = u_2
\end{aligned}
\qquad (6\text{-}8)
$$

and so last year's price takes on the burden that rainfall is supposed to carry in making the demand identifiable.

A very neat extension of Counting Rule 2 covers all these requirements: *For exact identification, the ranks of* A_a^{**} *and* $\tilde{A}_a^{**}$ *must equal* $G - 1$.

We can show this in a third way.[1] If, in the original model (6-7),

[1] With acknowledgments to T. C. Koopmans, in HOOD, pp. 31–32.

γ_{11} is truly nonzero, then it is impossible to construct a bogus demand equation without detecting it.   Take as the bogus demand

$$DD^{\oplus} = \tfrac{2}{3}DD + \tfrac{1}{3}SS$$

Then the bogus random term of demand is

$$u_2^{\oplus} = \frac{2u_1 + u_2}{3} - \frac{\gamma_{11}}{3}z_1$$

Then cov $(u_2^{\oplus}, z_1)$ is not zero, and will show up in estimation, unless the sample is the unlucky one in which rainfall is neutralized ($\tilde{\gamma}_{11} = 0$) by the random factor.   If, upon completing the estimation, we discover that $m_{\tilde{u}_2 \cdot z_1}$ is quite different from zero, then we can *detect* underidentification but we cannot remove it.   On the other hand, the discovery that $m_{\tilde{u}_2 \cdot z_1}$ is nearly zero is no guarantee that we have identified demand if there is a strong reason to suspect that supply is unaffected by rainfall.

6.9. Constraints on the stochastic assumptions

Let the random terms of (6-5) satisfy Simplifying Assumptions 1 to 7, so that cov $(u_1, u_2) = 0$.   Will this help to identify the supply SS? Sometimes.   Suppose that we knew beforehand that var u_1, cov (u_1, u_2), var u_2 were of the orders of magnitude 3, 0, 10, respectively.   The "deception" can be detected from (6-6) if $\Sigma(\tilde{\mu}_1^{\oplus})^2$, which is the estimate of var $u_1^{\oplus}$, is very different from 3.   This can have happened by chance in the sample used, but it becomes more and more unlikely the more $\Sigma(\tilde{\mu}_1^{\oplus})^2$ differs from 3.   On the other hand, the bogus variances and covariances may have nothing peculiar about them—indeed they may equal 3, 0, and 10, respectively, because of a special set of values that j, k, m, and n have taken on, for example, $j = \tfrac{1}{6}$, $k = \tfrac{1}{2}$, $m = -\tfrac{5}{3}$, $n = \tfrac{1}{6}$.   Therefore, in general, there is no guarantee that $SS^{\oplus}$ will look statistically different from SS, even if we have complete knowledge of the underlying covariances of the random term.

Another way to impose identification on a model is to say something specific about the variances of the random terms.   This was done by

Schultz in some early studies of agricultural markets.[1] In some of Schultz's work, both supply and demand are functions of the same two endogenous variables (price and quantity) and of random shocks. However, supply is more random than demand.   Then the scatter of observed points will be more in agreement with the demand than with the supply function.   Ambiguity is not eliminated entirely, but it is reduced as the randomness of supply increases relative to the randomness of demand.   In the notation of (6-6), the restriction takes the form var $u_1 = q$ var u_2; and identification improves with increase in q.

More complex restriction of this kind could also help.

To summarize the results of Secs. 6.7 to 6.9:

1. Identification can be checked before computing by use of the Counting Rules as applied to **A**.

2. If you fear that an equation is underidentified because you are not sure whether a given variable x reacts significantly, estimate the equation anyhow and then check whether the covariance of x with the residual $\tilde{u}_g$ is near zero; if not, you *may* have identified the gth equation. If $m_{x \cdot \tilde{u}_g}$ is near zero, you have *not* identified your equation.   If the numerically largest determinant of rank $G - 1$ from $\tilde{\mathbf{A}}_g^{**}$ is close to zero, x probably did not play a significant role.

3. There are tests that help *detect* underidentification.

4. It is sometimes possible to *remove* underidentification.

6.10. Identifiable parameters in an underidentified equation

When an equation is underidentified, is it perhaps possible to identify one or more of its parameters, though not all?   For instance, what about the identifiability of γ_{11} in (6-7)?   Intuition says that γ_{11} cannot be adulterated by linear combinations of DD, since z_1 occurs only in the supply SS.   Intuition is wrong if it concludes that this fact makes γ_{11} identifiable.   Applying (6-4), we have

$$-\gamma_{11} = \pi_{11} + \beta_{12}\pi_{21}$$

The πs can be computed from the reduced form

[1] Henry Schultz, *The Theory and Measurement of Demand*, pp. 72–81 (University of Chicago Press, Chicago: 1938).

$$y_1 = \pi_{11}z_1 + v_1$$
$$y_2 = \pi_{21}z_1 + v_2$$

but β_{12} is and remains unknown and, therefore, so does γ_{11}.

So, contrary to intuition, the fact that a given variable enters one equation of a model and no others does not make its coefficient identifiable. Underidentification is a disease affecting *all* parameters of the affected equation. For, if the gth equation is unidentified, this means that there are fewer equations than unknowns in the gth row of formula (6-4). All coefficients of the gth equation enter (6-4) symmetrically, and so none can have a privileged position over the others.

Let us now ask whether we can identify, in an otherwise unidentifiable equation, the *ratio* of two unidentifiable coefficients. In special cases it may be both important and sufficient to know the *relative* rather than the absolute impact of two kinds of variables. Let us consider (6-8) as a model of the supply and demand for loans, where y_1 is quantity of loans, y_2 is interest rate, z_1 is balances at the Federal Reserve, and z_2 is balances at foreign banks. We are curious to know whether the two kinds of bank balances differ in their effects on the loan policy of a commercial bank. Is it possible to identify γ_{11}/γ_{12}? No, because (6-4) applied to this model yields

$$-\gamma_{11} = \pi_{11} + \beta_{12}\pi_{21}$$
$$-\gamma_{12} = \pi_{12} + \beta_{12}\pi_{22}$$

which cannot be solved for γ_{11}/γ_{12} so long as β_{12} is unidentified. The most we can get is the relation

$$\frac{\gamma_{11} + \pi_{11}}{\pi_{21}} = \frac{\gamma_{12} + \pi_{12}}{\pi_{22}}$$

which is a straight line in the γ_{11},γ_{12} space, giving an infinity of pairs $(\gamma_{11},\gamma_{12})$.

Exercises

6.B Derive explicitly the equations $-\boldsymbol{\Gamma} = \mathbf{B}\boldsymbol{\Pi}$ for (6-8).

6.C In the above exercise, compute the two values of β_{21} in terms of the coefficients of the reduced form. Under what arithmetical conditions would they be identical? Interpret this in economic terms.

6.11. Source of ambiguity in overidentified models

Let us return to (6-8), rewriting it for convenience

$$SS \qquad q + \beta_{12}p + \gamma_{11}r + \gamma_{12}c = u_1$$
$$DD \qquad \beta_{21}q + \quad p \qquad\qquad = u_2 \qquad (6\text{-}9)$$

where q = quantity, p = price, r = rainfall, c = last year's price of a competing crop. Supply is underidentified, and demand is overidentified. For the latter we get from the reduced form two incompatible estimates of the single unknown β_{21}:

$$\beta'_{21} = \frac{-\check{\pi}_{21}}{\check{\pi}_{11}} \qquad \beta''_{21} = \frac{-\check{\pi}_{22}}{\check{\pi}_{12}}$$

But why should the reduced form, if estimated by least squares, give *two* values for β_{21}, the price elasticity of demand? The answer is in terms of the wobblings of the supply function. In (6-9), supply wobbles in response to random shocks u_1 and to two unrelated exogenous variables, this year's rainfall r and last year's price c of a competing crop. In Fig. 10a I have drawn some supply curves corresponding to different amounts of rainfall $(+1, -1)$ for a fixed value of c $(= 0)$. Observable points fall in the parallelogram $ABCD$. On the other hand, in Fig. 10b the variations in supply come not from rainfall (which is held constant at 0) but from last year's price only. Observations fall in the parallelogram $EFGH$. The first estimate of β

$$-\beta'_{21} = \frac{\check{\pi}_{21}}{\check{\pi}_{11}} = \frac{m_{(p,c)\cdot(r,c)}}{m_{(q,c)\cdot(r,c)}} \qquad (6\text{-}10)$$

corresponds to the broken line in Fig. 10a, because $\check{\pi}_{21}/\check{\pi}_{11}$ correlates price and quantity reactions as they result from variations in rainfall only. The other estimate

$$-\beta''_{21} = \frac{\check{\pi}_{22}}{\check{\pi}_{12}} = \frac{m_{(r,p)\cdot(r,c)}}{m_{(r,q)\cdot(r,c)}} \qquad (6\text{-}11)$$

corresponds to the broken line in Fig. 10b, because it correlates p to q as a result of variations in last year's price alone.[1] The sample must be very peculiar indeed that yields equal estimates β'_{21} and β''_{21}.

---

[1] In expressions like (6-10) and (6-11), the heuristic device of canceling the "factors" c and r in numerator and denominator gives a correct interpretation of what is being correlated, provided that these "factors" appear on both sides of both dots.

The explanation, then, is at bottom simple: When demand is overidentified, this means that both rainfall r and lagged price c make the supply shift up and down, and trace the demand relationship for us. The original form of the model shows this. The reduced form, however, does not allow us to trace the demand uniquely, as the result of the combined effect of rainfall and lagged price. Rather, the reduced form gives us a choice of estimating the slope of the demand equation *either* as a result of rainfall-induced variations in supply *or* as a result of lagged-price-induced variations in supply. Essentially, then, either alternative leaves out some crucial consideration, namely, the fact that

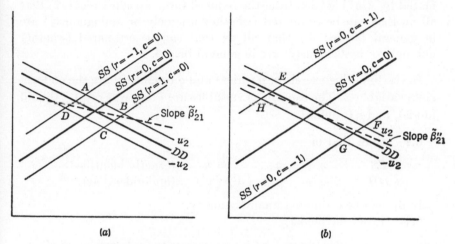

(a) (b)

Fig. 10. Ambiguity in an overidentified equation.

the omitted variable (lagged price and rainfall, respectively) also affects the price and quantity combinations that the sample shows.

To show that (6-10) is a biased estimate, write $p = u_2 - \beta_{21}q$. Then $m_{(p,c)\cdot(r,c)} = m_{(u_2,c)\cdot(r,c)} - \beta_{21}m_{(q,c)\cdot(r,c)}$, and so

$$-\beta_{21}' = -\beta_{21} + \frac{m_{(u_2,c)\cdot(r,c)}}{m_{(q,c)\cdot(r,c)}}$$

The expected value of the bias term is not zero. This is easily seen from (6-9). Let r, c, and u_1 be fixed, and let u_2 take on a set of conjugate values $+u_2$ and $-u_2 \neq 0$. Then, in (6-9), q necessarily takes on two different values q' and q'', and thus the above denominator changes as u_2 takes on its conjugate values. Therefore, $m_{(+u_2,c)\cdot(r,c)}/m_{(q',c)\cdot(r,c)}$ and $m_{(-u_2,c)\cdot(r,c)}/m_{(q'',c)\cdot(r,c)}$ do not add up to zero. To show that

β'_{21} is a consistent estimate, consider that Plim $m_{(u_2,c)\cdot(r,c)} = 0$ but Plim $m_{(q,c)\cdot(r,c)} \neq 0$.

Exercises

6.D If it turns out that $\beta'_{21} = \beta''_{21}$, the sample moments must satisfy either the equation $m_{rr}m_{cc} = m_{rc}m_{rc}$ or the equation $m_{pc}m_{qr} = m_{pr}m_{qc}$. The first of these declares that rainfall and last year's price are perfectly correlated in the sample. Interpret the second one. *Hint:* Use the fact that $p = u_2 - \beta_{21}q$.

6.E If least squares are applied to the reduced form, obtaining $\check{\pi}$s, prove the following: (1) that all parameters β, γ that can be estimated by working back from the reduced form are consistent; (2) that all γs that can be estimated (whether uniquely or ambiguously) are in general biased; (3) that all βs that can be estimated (whether uniquely or ambiguously) are in general biased.

In the following exercises, p (price) and q (quantity) are the endogenous variables. The exogenous variables are i (interest rate), f (liquid funds), and r (rainfall).

6.F Show that in

$$
\begin{array}{llll}
SS & q + \beta_{12}p & = u & \text{(exactly identified)} \\
DD & \beta_{21}q + p + \gamma_{21}i = v & & \text{(underidentified)}
\end{array}
$$

only β_{12} can be estimated unambiguously.

6.G From the model

$$
\begin{array}{llll}
SS & q + \beta_{12}p + & \gamma_{13}r = u & \text{(overidentified)} \\
DD & \beta_{21}q + p + \gamma_{21}i + \gamma_{22}f & = v & \text{(exactly identified)}
\end{array}
$$

the reduced form leads to the following estimates of β_{12}:

$$
-\beta'_{12} = \frac{\check{\pi}_{11}}{\check{\pi}_{21}} \qquad -\beta''_{12} = \frac{\check{\pi}_{12}}{\check{\pi}_{22}}
$$

where $\check{\pi}_{11} = m_{(q,f,r)\cdot(i,f,r)}/m_{(i,f,r)\cdot(i,f,r)}$ and $\check{\pi}_{21} = m_{(p,f,r)\cdot(i,f,r)}/m_{(i,f,r)\cdot(i,f,r)}$. Show that these estimates are biased and consistent.

6.H In Exercise 6.G, find the bias (if any) for $\check{\gamma}_{13}$, $\check{\gamma}_{21}$, $\check{\gamma}_{22}$.

6.12. Identification and the parameter space

The likelihood function $L(S)$ may or may not have a unique highest maximum as a function of the parameter estimates $\hat{\mathbf{A}}$. If it does, the model is (exactly or over-) identified.

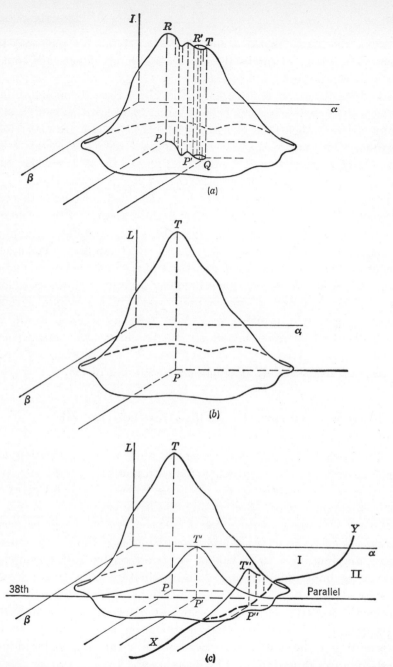

Fig. 11. Maxima of the likelihood function. *a.* Underidentified; *b.* exactly identified; *c.* overidentified.

Along the axes, labeled α and β in Fig. 11, let me represent the parameter space. Usually this space has more dimensions, but I cannot picture these on flat paper.

Underidentification is pictured in Fig. 11a. Here the mountain has either a flat top T or a ridge RR', or both. Its elevation is highest in many places rather than at a single place; i.e., there are many local maxima. This means that several values of α and β are candidates for the role of estimates of the true α and β. In the picture these candidates lie in the cobra-like area $PP'Q$ that creeps on the floor.

When the system is (exactly or over-) identified, nothing of this sort happens. The mountain has a single highest point. If the system is exactly identified, this fact is the end of the story, and Fig. 11b applies. When the system is overidentified, then Fig. 11c applies. The mountain in Fig. 11c is the same as in Fig. 11b, but we have several conflicting ways to look for the top. One estimating procedure allows us to look for the highest point of the mountain along, say, the 38th parallel; another equally admissible procedure tells us to look for it not along the 38th parallel but along the boundary XY between area I and area II. Accordingly, we get P' and P'', two estimates of P that correspond to β'_{21} and β''_{21} of equations (6-10) and (6-11).

6.13. Over- and underidentification contrasted

The example in the figure suggests that overidentification and underidentification are not simple logical opposites, except in a very trivial sense—in relation to the Counting Rules. Table 6.1 gives the contrasts among over-, exact, and underidentification.

We say that underidentification is not *usually* a stochastic property, because it arises from the *a priori* specification of the model and not from sampling, and so it cannot be removed by better sampling. Stochastic underidentification is in the nature of a freak; it was illustrated in Sec. 6.8. On the other hand, overidentification is a stochastic property that arises because we disregard some information contained in the sample. Overidentification is removed if *all* the information of the sample is utilized—which means that reduced-form least-squares estimation must be abandoned.

Table 6.1
Degree of identification

	UNDERIDENTIFI-CATION	EXACT IDENTIFICATION	OVERIDENTIFI-CATION
Unique maximum of the likelihood function	Does not exist	Exists	Exists
A *priori* restrictions for locating single highest point	Not enough	Enough	Too many
Ambiguity, if any, introduced because:	You have not enough independent variation in supply and demand	No ambiguity	In reduced form you disregard one or another cause in the variation of supply
Estimate of the parameters if based on reduced form βs	Biased, consistent	Biased, consistent	Biased, consistent
Estimate of the parameters if based on reduced form γs	Biased,* consistent	Biased,* consistent	Biased,* consistent
Is the degree of identification a stochastic property?	Not usually; yes, if in fact a variable fails to vary		Yes

* In special cases, unbiased.

6.14. Confluence

Multicollinearity and underidentification are two special cases of a mathematical property called *confluence*.

Multicollinearity arises when you cannot separate the effects of two (or more) theoretically independent variables because in your sample they happen to have moved together. This topic is taken up again in Chap. 9.

To show the connection between underidentification and multicollinearity, I shall use a model adapted from TINTNER, p. 33, which contains both.

Suppose that the world price of cotton is established by supply and demand conditions in the United States.   Let the supply of American cotton q depend only on its world price p, while the American demand for cotton depends both on its price and on national income y.

$$
\begin{aligned}
DD \qquad & q = \alpha p + \beta y + u \\
SS \qquad & q = \gamma p \qquad\;\; + v
\end{aligned}
\qquad (6\text{-}12)
$$

Now, demand in this model is underidentified.   If the sample comes

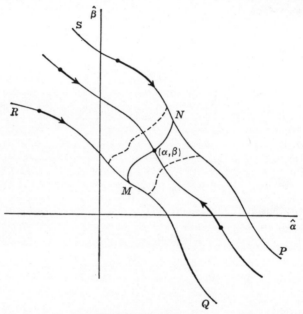

Fig. 12. Confluence.

from earlier years, when cotton was king, then the model, in addition, suffers from multicollinearity, because the national income was strongly correlated with the price and quantity of cotton.   In the parameter space for α, β, and γ, the likelihood function L has a stationary value over a region of the space $\alpha\beta\gamma$.   To picture this (Fig. 12) let us forget γ—or assume that someone has disclosed it to be $+0.03$.   The true value of the parameters is the point $(\alpha,\beta,0.03)$.   The ambiguous area, over which L has a flat top, is the band $PQRS$ in Fig. 12.   If a sample is taken from more recent years, multicollinearity is reduced, because national income y and the world price of cotton p are no longer so strongly correlated as before.   In Fig. 12, the gradual diversification of America's economy would appear as a gradual migration of the points in the band *PQRS* toward a narrower band around the curve *MN*.   If the time comes when cotton becomes quite insignificant, then multi-collinearity will have disappeared, but not the underidentification. In the figure, the band will have collapsed to the curve *MN*, *but not to a single point.*

Exercise

6.I   Suggest methods for removing multicollinearity and discuss them.

Digression on the etymology of the term "multicollinearity"

Suppose, for purposes of illustration only, that in (6-12) the true values of the parameters are simply $\alpha = -1, \beta = 1, \gamma = 1$. Also suppose that national income and the price of cotton are connected by the exact relation

$$y = 3p$$

(The exactness is for illustrative purposes only.   What follows is also true for the stochastic case $y = 3p + w$.)   Then the demand can be written

$$DD \qquad q = 2p + u$$

Now, the following estimates of α and β are consistent with all observations:

1. The true values $\alpha = -1, \beta = 1$
2. The pair of values $\alpha = 1, \beta = \frac{1}{3}$—because

$$q = 1p + \tfrac{1}{3}y + u = 2p + u$$

3. The pair of values $\alpha = 2, \beta = 0$; and an infinity of other pairs, which can be represented as the collinear points of line *AB* in Fig. 13

If we take a bogus demand function, then its parameters $\alpha^{\oplus}$, $\beta^{\oplus}$ also form a collinear set of points—like line *CD*—that agrees with the sample.

Removing multicollinearity causes *EF* to collapse into M, AB

into N, and CD into P; that is to say, removing multicollinearity collapses the band between the lines EF and CD into the line MNP. On the other hand, removing underidentification collapses the same band into the line AB.

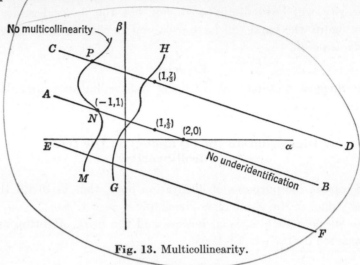

Fig. 13. Multicollinearity.

Further readings

KOOPMANS, chap. 17, extends and refines the concept of a complete model. The excellent introduction to identification, also by Koopmans, was cited in Sec. 6.1. KLEIN gives scattered examples with discussion (consult his index).

It is worthwhile to read the seminal article of Elmer J. Working, "What Do Statistical 'Demand Curves' Show?" (*Quarterly Journal of Economics*, vol. 41, no. 2, pp. 212–235, February, 1927), both for its contents and in order to appreciate how far econometrics has progressed since that time.

Trygve Haavelmo's treatment of confluence, in "The Probability Approach in Econometrics" (*Econometrica*, vol. 12, Supplement, 1944), is hard going, but an excellent exercise in decoding. If you have come this far, you can tackle this piece.

Those who appreciate the refinement and proliferation of concepts and are not afraid of flights into abstraction may glance at Leonid Hurwicz, "Generalization of the Concept of Identification," chap. 4 of KOOPMANS.

Herbert Simon, "Causal Order and Identifiability," in HOOD, chap. 3, shows how an econometric model can be analyzed into a hierarchy of submodels increasingly more endogenous and how the hierarchy accords with the statistical notion of causation and that of identifiability.

CHAPTER 7

Instrumental variables

7.1. Terminology and results

The term *instrumental variable* in econometrics has two entirely unrelated meanings:

1. A variable that can be manipulated at will by a policy maker as a tool or instrument of policy; for instance, taxes, the quantity of money, the rediscount rate

2. A variable, exogenous to the economy, significant, not entering the particular equation or equations we want to estimate, nevertheless used by us in a special way in estimating these equations

In this work only the second meaning is used.

This chapter explains and rationalizes the instrumental variable technique. It shows:

1. That the technique, though at first sight it appears odd, is logically similar to other estimating methods and also quite reasonable

2. That, if the choice of instrumental variables is unique, the model is exactly identified, and that the instrumental variable method is equivalent to applying least squares to the reduced form and then solving back to the original form

To understand the logic of instrumental variables we must first take a deep look at parameter estimation in general.

7.2. The rationale of estimating parametric relationships

Two ideas dominate the strategy of inferring parametric connections statistically. The first idea is that variables can be divided into causes and effects. The second is that conflicting observations must be weighted somehow.

Causes and effects

There can be one or more causes, symbolized by c, and one or more effects, symbolized by e. Various "instances" or "degrees" of c and e will carry a subscript. A parameter is nothing more than the change in effect(s), given a change in cause(s). Symbolically this can be represented as follows:

$$\text{Parameter} = \frac{\text{change in effect(s)}}{\text{corresponding change in cause(s)}} = \frac{\Delta e}{\Delta c} \qquad (7\text{-}1)$$

This relation[1] is fundamental in Chaps. 7 and 8; the general theme of these chapters is that all techniques of estimation are variations and elaborations of (7-1).

The change in cause(s) and effect(s) can be any change whatsoever. For instance, the change in effect e may be $e_1 - e_2$, or $e_2 - e_1$, or $e_{15} - e_{25}$; in general, $e_t - e_\theta$. The corresponding changes in cause c are $c_1 - c_2$, and $c_2 - c_1$, and $c_{15} - c_{25}$; in general, $c_t - c_\theta$.

Usually, however, the change is computed from some fixed reference level of the effect(s) or the cause(s)—and this fixed level is most typically the mean.[2] So parameters are usually computed by a formula like (7-2) rather than (7-1).

$$\text{Parameter estimate} = \frac{e_t - \bar{e}}{c_t - \bar{c}} = \tilde{\pi} \qquad (7\text{-}2)$$

---

[1] It is meant to be a conventional relationship. Only in the simplest linear systems is it true that the numerical value of a parameter can be expressed as simply as in equation (7-1).

[2] Ideally, the mean *of the population*. In practice, the mean *of the sample*. In linear models the distinction is immaterial for most purposes.

This is merely a convenience, which does not affect the logic of parameter estimation. Henceforth, all symbols Δe, Δc, e_t, c_t, or simply e and c represent deviations from the corresponding mean.

The problem of conflicting observations

What happens when two or more applications of (7-2) give different values for $\tilde{\pi}$? This is very likely to happen in stochastic models, because in such models the effect e results not merely from the explicit cause c but also from the disturbance u. Which of the several conflicting values should be assigned to the unknown parameter π? The problem arises in all but the simplest cases of parameter estimation.

In general, the parameter estimate is a weighted average of quotients of the form e/c. Take the model $e_t = \gamma c_t + u_t$. Then the weighted estimate of γ is

$$\tilde{\gamma} = \frac{e_1}{c_1} w_1 + \frac{e_2}{c_2} w_2 + \cdots + \frac{e_s}{c_s} w_s$$

Any set of weights w_1, w_2, . . . , w_s will do, provided they add up to 1. If you want to attach much significance to the instance e_{12}/c_{12}, make w_{12} large; if you want to disregard the instance e_{27}/c_{27}, make $w_{27} = 0$ or even negative.

Let us for simplicity restrict ourselves to just two observations. One of the many possible sets of weights is the following:

$$w_1 = \frac{c_1^2}{c_1^2 + c_2^2} \qquad w_2 = \frac{c_2^2}{c_1^2 + c_2^2} \tag{7-3}$$

Then, using these weights, the weighted estimate is also the familiar least squares estimate, because

$$\tilde{\gamma} = \frac{e_1}{c_1} \frac{c_1^2}{c_1^2 + c_2^2} + \frac{e_2}{c_2} \frac{c_2^2}{c_1^2 + c_2^2} = \frac{e_1 c_1 + e_2 c_2}{c_1^2 + c_2^2} = \frac{m_{ec}}{m_{cc}} = \check{\gamma}$$

So the least squares estimate amounts to nothing more than a special method for weighting conflicting values of the ratios e/c. Now two questions arise: (1) Why should the weights (7-3) be functions of the c's or have anything at all to do with the cause c? and (2) why should we pick those particular formulas and not, for example, absolute values

$$w_1 = \frac{|c_1|}{|c_1| + |c_2|} \qquad w_2 = \frac{|c_2|}{|c_1| + |c_2|} \tag{7-4}$$

or cubes, square roots, or logarithms?

The answer to question 1 is that the more strongly the cause departs from its average level, the more you weight it. It is as though we said that the real test of the relationship $e_t = \gamma c_t + u_t$ is whether it stands up under atypical, nonaverage conditions (i.e., when c_t is far from $\bar{c}$).

But now why should one [as formulas (7-3) and (7-4) suggest] give equal weight to $+c_t$ and $-c_t$? The common-sense rationale here is that *the same credence* should be given to a ratio e/c when c is atypically small (relative to its mean) as when it is atypically large. This requirement is met by an evenly increasing function of c, for instance:

$$\frac{|c|}{\Sigma|c|} \qquad \frac{c^2}{\Sigma c^2} \qquad \frac{|c^3|}{\Sigma|c^3|} \qquad \frac{c^4}{\Sigma c^4} \qquad \frac{\sqrt{|c|}}{\Sigma \sqrt{|c|}} \qquad \frac{\log c^2}{\Sigma \log c^2} \tag{7-5}$$

The answer to question (2) is this: From the many alternative formulas in (7-5), $c^2/\Sigma c^2$ is selected because of the assumption that u is normally distributed, in which case least squares approaches maximum likelihood. A different probability distribution of the disturbances would prescribe a different set of weights for averaging or reconciling conflicting values of e/c.

7.3. A single instrumental variable

With these preliminaries well digested, we are ready to understand the logic of instrumental variables. Suppose that

$$p_t = \beta q_t + u_t \tag{7-6}$$

is a model for the demand for sugar. This equation is known to have come from a larger system in which p (price) and q (quantity) are endogenous and a great many other causes are active. We call (7-6) the *manifest* model and all the remaining relationships the *latent* model. Suppose that z represents some exogenous cause affecting the economy, say, the tax on steel. Now in an interdependent economic system the tax on steel affects theoretically both the price of sugar and the quantity of sugar bought, because a tax cannot leave unaffected either the price or the quantity of any substitute or competitive goods, and sugar surely must be somewhere at the end of the chain of substitutes or complements of steel.

The method of instrumental variables says that you ought to compute an estimate of γ (from two observations $s = 1, 2$) as follows:

$$\tilde{\gamma} = \frac{p_1}{q_1} w_1 + \frac{p_2}{q_2} w_2 \qquad (7\text{-}7)$$

using as weights

$$w_1 = \frac{q_1 z_1}{q_1 z_1 + q_2 z_2} \qquad w_2 = \frac{q_2 z_2}{q_1 z_1 + q_2 z_2} \qquad (7\text{-}8)$$

so that the estimate of γ is

$$\tilde{\gamma} = \frac{p_1}{q_1} \frac{q_1 z_1}{q_1 z_1 + q_2 z_2} + \frac{p_2}{q_2} \frac{q_2 z_2}{q_1 z_1 + q_2 z_2} = \frac{p_1 z_1 + p_2 z_2}{q_1 z_1 + q_2 z_2} = \frac{m_{zp}}{m_{zq}} \qquad (7\text{-}9)$$

Every ounce of common sense in you ought to rear itself in rebellion at this perpetration. You ought to protest, saying: "Nonsense! My boss at the Zachary Sugar Refinery will fire me unceremoniously from my well-paid and respected job of Company Econometrician if I tell the Vice-President that I multiply the price and quantity of sugar with the tax on steel to estimate demand for sugar! Better give me a good argument for this act of alchemy. Moreover, did it ever occur to you that m_{zq} in the denominator could *conceivably* be equal to zero— and *certainly* is in some samples?[1] This predicament could not arise in leastsquare weights like (7-3)."

I hasten to reply to the last point first. The possibility that m_{qz} might be zero is the reason why z should not be chosen haphazardly but rather from exogenous variables that have a lot to do with the quantity of sugar consumed. So, instead of the tax on steel, perhaps we ought to take the tax on coffee, honey, or sugar, or the quantity of school lunches financed by Congress. Still, it is possible that, *in the sample chosen*, the quantity of sugar q and the quantity of school lunches z happen to be uncorrelated, and it is true that this sort of difficulty is unheard of in least squares, because m_{qq} just cannot be zero: the quantity of sugar is perfectly correlated with itself.

---

[1] This sample would be a set of measure zero, as the mathematicians say.

Now what do the weights (7-9) say? They say that, the more sugar consumption and school lunches move together,[1] the more weight should be given to $\Delta p/\Delta q$, the price effect of the change in the quantity consumed. There is another way to look at this matter: Write, purely heuristically,

$$\beta = \frac{\Delta p}{\Delta q} = \frac{\Delta p/\Delta z}{\Delta q/\Delta z} \tag{7-10}$$

where $\Delta p/\Delta z$ is symbolized by γ_1 and $\Delta q/\Delta z$ by γ_2. How could we possibly interpret γ_1 and γ_2?

Figure 14 represents both the *latent* and the *manifest* parts of the

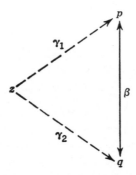

Fig. 14. The logic of the instrumental variable.

model (7-6). The solid arrow represents the manifest mutual causation $p \leftrightarrow q$, which appears in (7-6). The broken arrows represent the latent model, which is not spelled out but which states that z affects p and q through the workings of the whole economic system. So the meaning of γ_1 and γ_2 is that they are the coefficients of the latent model. Since z is exogenous, why not estimate γ_1 and γ_2 by least squares? It sounds highly reasonable. There should be no objection to this.

$$\breve{\gamma}_1 = \frac{m_{zp}}{m_{zz}} \qquad \breve{\gamma}_2 = \frac{m_{zq}}{m_{zz}} \tag{7-11}$$

Insert (7-11) in (7-10), and then

$$\breve{\beta} = \frac{\Delta p/\Delta z}{\Delta q/\Delta z} = \frac{\breve{\gamma}_1}{\breve{\gamma}_2} = \frac{m_{zp}/m_{zz}}{m_{zq}/m_{zz}} = \frac{m_{zp}}{m_{zq}} \tag{7-12}$$

which justifies the instrumental variable formula (7-9).

[1] In a given instance, not over-all.

It is well to ask now: in what way do the two examples $p = \beta q + u$ and $e = \gamma c + u$ differ? Why may the second model be computed by least squares although the first has to be estimated by instrumental variables? The reason is that the second $c \to e$ is a complete model in itself: causation flows from c to e, and nothing else is involved. On the other hand, $p = \beta q + u$ hides a lot of complexity, i.e., causation from z to p and from z to q. These causations are unidirectional $z \dashrightarrow p$ and $z \dashrightarrow q$ and can be treated like $c \to e$; but $p \leftrightarrow q$ is not of the same kind, and must be treated by taking into account the hidden part.

7.4. Connection with the reduced form

The instrumental variable technique is very intimately connected with the method of applying least squares to the reduced form. Assume for the moment that z is the only exogenous variable affecting the economy and that the complete model is

$$
\begin{aligned}
p - \beta q &= u \\
\frac{1}{\gamma_1}p + \frac{1}{\gamma_2}q - z &= v
\end{aligned}
\tag{7-13}
$$

whose first equation is manifest (the solid arrows in Fig. 14). The second equation is latent and corresponds to the broken arrows.

Exercise

7.A Explain why the complete model cannot contain *three* independent equations, one for $p \leftrightarrow q$, one for $z \dashrightarrow p$, and one for $z \dashrightarrow q$. The reduced form is

$$
\begin{aligned}
Dp &= \beta z + \frac{1}{\gamma_2} u + \beta v \\
Dq &= z - \frac{1}{\gamma_1} u + v
\end{aligned}
\tag{7-14}
$$

where D is the determinant $1/\gamma_2 + \beta/\gamma_2$.

If the second equation in (7-13) contained another exogenous variable, say, z', then the first equation would be overidentified. This fact would be reflected in the instrumental variable technique as the following dilemma: Should we use z or z' as the instrumental variable? On this last point I have more to say in Secs. 7.5 to 7.7.

7.5. Properties of the instrumental variable technique in the simplest case

The technique is biased and consistent, where naïve least squares is biased and inconsistent.

$$\tilde{\beta} = \frac{m_{zp}}{m_{zq}} = \beta + \frac{m_{zu}}{m_{zq}} = \beta + \frac{1}{D} \frac{m_{zu}}{m_{zz} - (1/\gamma_1)m_{zu} + m_{zv}} \tag{7-15}$$

$$\beta = \frac{m_{qp}}{m_{qq}} = \beta + \frac{m_{qu}}{m_{qq}}$$

$$= \beta + \frac{1}{D} \frac{m_{zu} - (1/\gamma_1)m_{uu} + m_{vu}}{m_{zz} - (2/\gamma_1)m_{zu} + 2m_{zv} + (1/\gamma_1^2)m_{uu} - (2/\gamma_1)m_{vu} + m_{vv}} \tag{7-16}$$

Under the ordinary Simplifying Assumptions, $\sigma_{zu} = \sigma_{zv} = \sigma_{vu} = 0$; so, for large samples, the first expression approaches β, and the second approaches

$$\beta - \frac{1}{D} \frac{\gamma_1 \sigma_{uu}}{\gamma_1^2 \sigma_{zz} + \sigma_{uu} + \gamma_1^2 \sigma_{vv}} \neq \beta$$

Expression (7-15) gives us additional guidance for selecting an instrumental variable. To minimize bias, the following conditions should be fulfilled, either singly or in combination:

1. m_{zu} numerically small
2. m_{zz} numerically large
3. D numerically large

The first condition says that z should be truly exogenous to the sugar market. Appropriations for school lunches are better in this respect than the tax on sugar, because the tax might have been imposed to discourage consumption or to maximize revenue, in which case it would have some connection with the parameters and variables of the sugar market.

The second condition says that, in the sample, the instrumental variable must have varied a lot: if the tax on sugar varied only trivially it had no opportunity to affect p and q significantly enough for us to capture β by our estimating procedure. From this point of view the tax on sugar might be less desirable as an instrumental variable than some remote but more volatile entity, say, the budget's appropriations for U.S. Information Service.

The third condition says that $D = 1/\gamma_2 + \beta/\gamma_1$ should be numerically large; that is, that γ_1 and γ_2 should be numerically small relative to β. This says that, to minimize bias, p and q should react more strongly to each other (in the manifest model) than to the instrumental variable in the latent model. It requires that price and quantity be more sensitive to each other in the sugar market than to such things as the U.S.I.S. budget, the tax on honey, or, for that matter, the tax on sugar itself.

It is not easy to find an instrumental variable fulfilling all these conditions at once. However, if the sample is large, any sort of instrumental variable gives better estimates than least squares.

7.6. Extensions

The instrumental variable technique can be extended in several directions:

1. The single-equation incomplete manifest model may contain several parameters to be estimated. For example, the model $p = \beta_1 q + \beta_2 y + u$ requires two instrumental variables z_1 and z_2.

The estimating formulas are analogous to (7-9):

$$\tilde{\beta}_1 = \frac{m_{(z_1,z_2)(p,y)}}{m_{(z_1,z_2)(q,y)}} \qquad \tilde{\beta}_2 = \frac{m_{(z_1,z_2)(q,p)}}{m_{(z_1,z_2)(q,y)}} \tag{7-17}$$

All the criteria of Sec. 7.5 for selecting a good instrumental variable are still valid, plus the following: z_1 and z_2 must really be different variables, that is, variables not well correlated in the sample; else the denominators approach zero, and the estimates $\tilde{\beta}_1$, $\tilde{\beta}_2$ blow up.

Exercise

7.B If we wish to estimate the parameters of $p = \beta q + \gamma z + u$, where z is exogenous, is it permissible for z itself to be one of the instrumental variables z_1 and z_2?

2. The incomplete manifest model may consist of several equations,

for instance:

$$p + \beta_{12}q + \beta_{13}y \quad\quad = u_1$$
$$\beta_{21}p + \quad q \quad\quad + \gamma_2 z = u_2$$

Each equation can be estimated independently of the other, using formulas analogous to (7-17). Variable z itself and another variable z_1 may be used as instrumental variables in both equations, or two variables z_1, z_2 completely extraneous to the manifest model may be used.

7.7. How to select instrumental variables

In some instances we may have several candidates for the role of instrumental variable. The choice is made anew for each equation of the manifest model, and the rules are:

1. If several instrumental variables are needed, they should be those least correlated with one another.

2. The instrumental variables should affect strongly as many as possible of the variables present in the equation that is being estimated.

Choosing instrumental variables is admittedly arbitrary. Another statistician with the same data might make a different choice and so get different results for the same model. The technique of *weighting instrumental variables* eliminates some of this arbitrariness. I illustrate the technique for the single-equation, single-parameter demand model $p = \beta q + u$. Suppose that two exogenous variables are available, z_1 (the sugar tax) and z_2 (the tax on honey), and that both affect p and q. To select z_1 or z_2 is arbitrary. The new variable $z = w_1 z_1 + w_2 z_2$, a linear combination of the two taxes with arbitrary weights w_1 and w_2, is less arbitrary because both taxes are taken into account.[1]

Results improve considerably if we take w_1, w_2 proportional to the importance of the two taxes on the sugar market. Naturally, to estimate the parameters of the sugar market, the weight given the sugar tax should be greater than that given to the tax on honey; and vice versa when we want to study the honey market. In general, we ought to rank the instrumental variable candidates z_1, z_2, z_3, . . . in order of increasing remoteness from the sector being estimated and

[1] This treatment with $w_1 = w_2 = 1$ coincides with Theil's method with $k = 1$. Consult Chap. 9 below.

assign them decreasing weights in a new instrumental variable $z = w_1 z_1 + w_2 z_2 + w_3 z_3 + \cdots$. The more accurate the *a priori* information by means of which weights are assigned, the more does this technique approximate the results of the full information maximum likelihood method, discussed in Chap. 8.

Exercises
Warning: These are difficult!

7.C Prove or disprove the conjecture that weighted instrumental variables are "better" than unweighted.   Use the model $p = \beta q + u$, $(1/\gamma_1)p + (1/\gamma_2)q - \delta_1 z_1 - \delta_2 z_2 = v$, where γ_1, γ_2, δ_1, δ_2 measure the sensitivity of p and q to z_1 and z_2.   Define w_1 and w_2 as $\delta_1/(\delta_1 + \delta_2)$. Define

$$\tilde{\beta}(z_1) = \frac{m_{z_1 p}}{m_{z_1 q}}$$

$$\tilde{\beta}(z_2) = \frac{m_{z_2 p}}{m_{z_2 q}}$$

$$\tilde{\beta}(z) = \frac{m_{(w_1 z_1 + w_2 z_2) \cdot p}}{m_{(w_1 z_1 + w_2 z_2) \cdot q}}$$

Prove $\varepsilon\{\tilde{\beta}(z_1) - \varepsilon[\tilde{\beta}(z_1)]\}^2 > \varepsilon\{\tilde{\beta}(z) - \varepsilon[\tilde{\beta}(z)]\}^2 < \varepsilon\{\tilde{\beta}(z_2) - \varepsilon[\tilde{\beta}(z_2)]\}^2$.

7.D Prove or disprove the conjecture that the goodness of the weighted instrumental variable technique is insensitive to small departures of w_1, w_2 from their ideal relative sizes $\delta_1/(\delta_1 + \delta_2)$, $\delta_2/(\delta_1 + \delta_2)$.

CHAPTER 8

Limited information

8.1. Introduction

Limited information maximum likelihood is one of the many techniques available for estimating an identified (exactly or overidentified) equation. Other methods are (1) naïve least squares, (2) least squares applied to the reduced form, (3) instrumental variables, (4) weighted instrumental variables, (5) Theil's method,[1] and (6) full information.

Method 1 is biased and inconsistent; the rest are biased and consistent. They are listed in order of increasing efficiency. Limited information leads to burdensome computations, but is less cumbersome than full information. Unlike full information but like all other methods, limited information can be used on one equation of a model at a time. Limited information differs from the method of instrumental variables in two ways: it makes use of all, not an arbitrary selection, of the exogenous variables affecting the system; it prescribes a special way of using the exogenous variables. If an equation is exactly identified, limited information and instrumental variables are equivalent methods. Like *all* methods of estimating parameters, limited information uses formulas that are nothing more than a

[1] Discussed in Chap. 9.

glorified version of the quotient

$$\frac{\text{Change in effect(s)}}{\text{Corresponding change in cause(s)}}$$

I shall illustrate by the example of (8-1), where the first equation is to be estimated by the limited information method. The rest of the model may be either latent or manifest. The limited information method ignores part of what goes on in the remaining equations by deliberate choice, not because they are latent (though, of course, they might be). However, in (8-1) the entire model is spelled out for pedagogic reasons. The minus signs are contrary to the notational conventions used so far but are very handy in solving for y_1, y_2, y_3. Nothing in the logic of the situation is changed by expressing $\mathbf{B}$ and $\boldsymbol{\Gamma}$ in negative terms.

$$
\begin{aligned}
y_1 - \beta y_2 \quad & \quad - \gamma z_1 \quad & = u_1 \\
y_2 - \beta_{23} y_3 \quad & \quad - \gamma_{22} z_2 - \gamma_{23} z_3 - \gamma_{24} z_4 & = u_2 \quad (8\text{-}1) \\
-\beta_{31} y_1 \quad + \quad y_3 - \gamma_{31} z_1 \quad & \quad - \gamma_{34} z_4 & = u_3
\end{aligned}
$$

As usual, a single asterisk distinguishes the variables admitted in the first equation and a double asterisk those excluded from it. Thus $\mathbf{y}^* = \text{vec}\,(y_1, y_2)$, $\mathbf{z}^* = \text{vec}\,(z_1)$, $\mathbf{y}^{**} = \text{vec}\,(y_3)$, $\mathbf{z}^{**} = \text{vec}\,(z_2, z_3, z_4)$.

We apply the limited information method in two cases:

1. When nothing more is known about the economy than that somehow z_2, z_3, z_4 affect it
2. When more is known but this is purposely ignored

8.2. The chain of causation

Let the first equation be the one we wish to estimate, out of a model containing several. The chains of causation in a general model of several equations in several unknowns are shown in Fig. 15. The arrowheads show that causation flows from the z's to the y's but not back, and mutually between the y's. Solid arrows correspond to the first equation, broken arrows to the rest of the model. The two left-hand rounded arrows, one solid, one broken, show that the y^*'s (the endogenous variables admitted in the manifest model) interact both in the first equation and (possibly, too) in the rest of the model. The right-

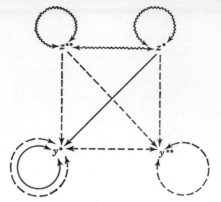

Fig. 15. Causation in econometric models.

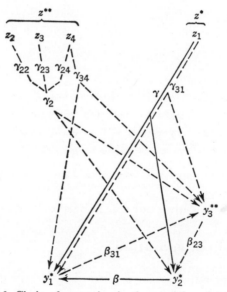

Fig. 16. Chain of causation in the special model (8-1).

hand rounded arrow shows that the y^{**}'s (the endogenous variables excluded) interact, but, naturally, only in the rest of the model.

Parenthetically, the crinkly arrows symbolize intercorrelation among the exogenous variables. Ideally, the exogenous variables are unconnected, but in any given sample they may happen to be intercorrelated. This is the familiar problem of multicollinearity (Sec. 6.14) in its general form.   The stronger the correlation between one z and another, the less reliable are estimates of the γs because different exogenous variables have acted alike in the sample period.   We shall ignore multicollinearity and continue with the main subject.

Figure 16 shows the chains of causation in (8-1).   The variable z_1 affects y_1 and y_2 in the first equation and y_1 and y_3 in the third. Variables z_2, z_3, z_4 affect y_2 and y_3 in the second, and z_4 affects y_1 and y_3 in the third.   We can make the arrows between the y's single rather than double-headed because there are as many equations as there are endogenous variables.   Thus the model can be put into *cyclical form*.[1] It so happens that (8-1) is already in this form; that is, given a constellation of values for the exogenous variables and the random disturbances, if we give y_3 an arbitrary value, then y_3 determines y_2, which in turn determines y_1, which in turn affects y_3, and so round and round until mutually compatible values are reached.

8.3. The rationale of limited information

The problem of estimating the model of Fig. 16 can be likened to the following problem.   Suppose that z_1, z_2, z_3, z_4 are the locations of four springs of water and that y_1, y_2, y_3 are, respectively, the kitchen tap, bathtub tap, and shower tap of a given house.   The arrows are pipes or presumed pipes.   Estimating the first equation is like trying to find the width of the pipes between z_1 and y_1 and y_2 and of the pipe between y_2 and y_1.   The width is estimated by varying the flows at the four springs z_1, z_2, z_3, z_4 and then measuring the resulting flow in the kitchen (y_1), bathtub (y_2), and shower (y_3).   Limited information attempts to solve the same problem with the following handicaps arising either from lack of knowledge or from deliberate neglect of knowledge:

1. Pipes are known to exist for certain only where there are solid arrows (γ, β).

2. It is known that z_2, z_3, z_4 enter the flow somewhere or other, but it is not known where.

3. It is not known whether there is another direct pipeline (γ_{31}) from z_1 to the kitchen (y_1) and bathtub (y_2).

4. The flow at the shower (y_3) is ignored even if it is measurable.

[1] Note carefully that the *cyclical* and the *recursive* are different forms.

So as not to fill up page upon page with dull arithmetic, I am going to cut model (8-1) drastically by some special assumptions, which, I vouch, remove nothing essential from the problem. The special assumptions are: $\beta = 1.6$, $\gamma = 0.5$, $\gamma_{31} = \gamma_{34} = 0$, $\beta_{31} = 0.1$, $\beta_{23} = 2$; $\gamma_{22}z_2 + \gamma_{23}z_3 + \gamma_{24}z_4$ is combined into one simple term $= \gamma_2z^{**}$; $\gamma_2 = 0.5$.   Then (8-1) collapses to

$$
\begin{aligned}
y_1 - \beta y_2 \qquad\qquad - \gamma z_1^* \qquad\qquad &= u_1 \\
y_2 - \beta_{23}y_3 \qquad\qquad - \gamma_2 z^{**} &= u_2 \\
-\beta_{31}y_1 \qquad\quad + \quad y_3 \qquad\qquad &= u_3
\end{aligned}
\qquad (8\text{-}2)
$$

and Fig. 16 collapses to Fig. 17.   Now let us change metaphors.

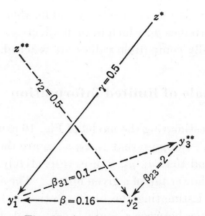

Fig. 17. Another special case.

Instead of a hydraulic system, think of a telephone network. The coefficients β, γ, if greater than 1, represent loud-speakers; if less than 1, low-speakers.   Where a coefficient is equal to 1, sound is transmitted exactly.   To avoid having to reconcile conflicting observations, assume that all the disturbances are zero, i.e., that there is neither leakage of sound out of nor noise into the acoustic system of Fig. 17.

Here is how the estimating procedure works.   Begin from a state of acoustical equilibrium, and measure the noise level at each point of the network.   Then step up the sound level at z^{**} by 100 units. Only 50 of these reach location y_2, because there is a twofold low-speaker ($\gamma_2 = 0.5$) between z^{**} and y_2.   Also step up the sound level at z_1^* by, say, 10 units.   Only 5 units ($\gamma = 0.5$) get to y_1.   But, whatever extra noise there is at y_1, one-tenth of it ($\beta_{31} = 0.1$) reaches y_3. From y_3 a loud-speaker doubles the increment as it conveys it to y_2, whence some gets to y_1, and so on. By differencing (8-2) and solving for $\Delta u = 0$, $\Delta z^* = 10$, and $\Delta z^{**} = 100$, the ultimate increments are found to be $\Delta y_1 = 125, \Delta y_2 = 75, \Delta y_3 = 12.5$. Now, suppose we did not know how strong was the low-speaker connection β between y_1 and y_2. By differencing (8-2), we get

$$\beta = \frac{\Delta y_1 - \gamma \, \Delta z^*}{\gamma_2 \, \Delta z^{**} + \beta_{23}\beta_{31} \, \Delta y_1} \tag{8-3}$$

When the model is exact, it takes exactly five observations to determine β, γ, γ_2, β_{23}, β_{31}. When the model is stochastic, there are complications, but the basic appearance of the formula is not much different. The numerator can be interpreted as that change in the sound level y_1 not attributable to what is coming over the line from z^*, that is to say, only the sound that comes from y_2 and y_3. The denominator measures the increment at y_2 resulting from two sources z^{**} and y_3. The limited information method just ignores the latter source entirely. This is so because both β_{23} and β_{31} belong to the "rest of the model" and are neither specified nor evaluated. So, (8-3) is interpreted as follows:

$$\beta = \frac{\text{variation in } y_1^* \text{ not due to any } z^*}{\text{variation in } y_2^* \text{ from all sources}} \tag{8-4}$$

The limited information method suppresses β_{23} and β_{31} and estimates β by

$$\beta = \frac{\Delta y_1 - \gamma \, \Delta z^*}{\gamma_2 \, \Delta z^{**}} = \frac{\text{variation in } y_1^* \text{ not due to } z^*}{\text{variation in } y_2^* \text{ due to } z^{**}} \tag{8-5}$$

Notice carefully that the method suppresses only β_{23}, β_{31}, that is, the latent model's intervariation of the *endogenous* variables. It does *not* suppress γ_2, i.e., the variation (in the latent model) due to the *exogenous* variables z^{**}.

8.4. Formulas for limited information

This section shows that the lengthy formulas for computing limited information estimates are just fancy versions of (8-3). It can safely be skipped, for it contains no new ideas. To obtain estimates of the

βs of the first equation, combine the moments of the variables as in the following list:

In general   *In model* (8-1)

1. Construct

$$C = m_{y^*z}(m_{zz})^{-1}m_{zy^*}$$

$$m_{(y_1,y_2)(z_1,z_2,z_3,z_4)} \cdot \{m_{(z_1,z_2,z_3,z_4)}{}^2\}^{-1}$$
$$\cdot \, m_{(z_1,z_2,z_3,z_4)(y_1,y_2)}$$

2. Construct

$$D = m_{y^*z^*}\{m_{z^*z^*}\}^{-1}m_{z^*y^*}$$

$$\begin{bmatrix} m_{y_1z_1} \\ m_{y_2z_1} \end{bmatrix} \cdot (m_{z_1z_1})^{-1} \cdot (m_{z_1y_1} \quad m_{z_1y_2})$$

3. Construct

$$W = m_{y^*y^*} - C$$

$$\begin{bmatrix} m_{y_1y_1} & m_{y_1y_2} \\ m_{y_2y_1} & m_{y_2y_2} \end{bmatrix} - C$$

4. Compute[1]

$$V = C - D$$

5. Compute[2]

$$Q = V^{-1}W$$

6. The estimate of the βs of the first equation is a nontrivial solution (called the *eigenvector*) of Q.

7. Having computed β, one can calculate $\hat{\gamma}$, $\hat{u}$, and estimates of the covariances of the disturbances and the parameter estimates.

In steps 1 and 2 above, the factors $m_{z^*z^*}$ and m_{zz} and also the z and z^* in the remaining moment matrices play a role analogous to the weights $c_i^2/\Sigma c_i^2$ in the least squares technique.[3] They just provide a method for reconciling the conflicting observations generated by the nonzero random disturbances.

The matrix $m_{y^*y^*}$ corresponds to the pair of round arrows about y^* in Fig. 15.

Essentially, Q is an estimate of the βs of the first equation. Q can be interpreted as a quotient, because the matrix operation $V^{-1}W$ reminds one of the ratio of two numbers: W/V. Actually, this impressionistic intuition is quite correct. W corresponds to an elaborate case of Δe

---

[1] KLEIN calls this B instead of V. I use V to avoid confusion with the B of $By + \Gamma z = u$.

[2] KLEIN calls this A. I use Q to avoid confusion with the A of the model $Ax = u$.

[3] Compare with Sec. 7.2.

(the change in the effects), and V is an elaborate case of Δc (the corresponding change in the causes). Indeed W and V are complicated cases of the numerator and denominator of (8-5). W is interpreted as the variation of the endogenous variables not due to any exogenous changes, and V expresses the variation of the endogenous variables from all sources exogenous to any equation of the model and endogenous to the manifest part.

8.5. Connection with the instrumental variable method

Limited information recognizes that exogenous influences not present in the first equation influence the course of events. The instrumental variable method acknowledges the same thing. Limited information makes use of *all* these exogenous influences, whereas the instrumental variable method (generally) *picks* from among them, either haphazardly or according to the principles of Sec. 7.7.

When the first equation is exactly identified, picking is impossible and the two methods coincide.

8.6. Connection with indirect least squares

The limited information method can also be interpreted as a form of modified indirect least squares or as a generalization of directional least squares (see the Digression in Sec. 4.4). The direct or naïve least squares method estimates β essentially as the regression coefficient of y_1 on y_2. Haavelmo's proposition (Chap. 4) advised us to minimize square residuals in the northeast-southwest direction in order to allow for autonomous variations in the exogenous variable, investment z_t. In (8-1) there are several such exogenous variables z_1, z_2, z_3, z_4 which generate in the $y_1 y_2$ plane a scatter diagram which is a weighted average of lozenge-shaped figures (as in Fig. 9), one for z_1, one for z_2, and so on. In matrix C (and, hence, in W and V) this weighted averaging has taken place.

Further readings

Hood, chap. 10, describes in detail how to compute limited information and other types of estimates, and illustrates with a completely worked out macroeconomic model of Klein's.

CHAPTER 9

The family of simultaneous estimating techniques

9.1. Introduction

We owe to Theil[1] a theorem showing that all the estimating techniques of Chaps. 4 to 8 are special cases of a new technique, which has the further merit of being fairly easy to compute. Section 9.2, which covers this ground, is addressed primarily to lovers of mathematical generality and elegance; other readers might skip or skim.

The other sections of this chapter reconsider underidentification and overidentification from the point of view of research strategy. Section 9.3 accepts models as given (over-, under-, or exactly identified) and suggests alternative treatments. Section 9.4 raises the issue of whether econometric models can be anything but underidentified.

9.2. Theil's method of dual reduced forms

This method can be applied to all equations of a system, one at a time. The equation we want to estimate, called the "first" equation,

---

[1] Reference in Further Readings at the end of this chapter.

comes from a complete system, for instance, (8-1). We know and can observe *all* the exogenous variables affecting the system, and we also know *a priori* which variables (endogenous and exogenous) enter the first equation. The other equations may be identified or not. The disturbances have the usual Simplifying Properties. Any endogenous variable of the first equation can be chosen to play the role of dependent variable. We shall use y_1 in this role. The remaining variables of the first equation, namely, $y_2, \ldots, y_{G^*}; z_1, \ldots, z_{H^*}$, must all be different in the sample; that is to say, they must not behave as if they were linear combinations of one another. We do not need to know or observe the endogenous variables $y_{G^*+1}, \ldots, y_G$ not present in the first equation.

Let one star, as usual, represent presence in the first equation, and two stars, absence from the first equation.

We then form *two* reduced forms whose coefficients we calculate by simple least squares: (1) $\mathbf{y}^*$ on $\mathbf{z}^*$ with parameters $\check{\pi}$ and residuals v; and (2) $\mathbf{y}^*$ on $\mathbf{z} = (\mathbf{z}^*, \mathbf{z}^{**})$ with parameters $\check{\rho}$ and residuals w. For instance, to estimate the first equation of (8-1), compute

$$
\begin{aligned}
y_1 &= \check{\pi}_{11} z_1 + \check{v}_1 & y_1 &= \check{\rho}_{11} z_1 + \check{\rho}_{12} z_2 + \check{\rho}_{13} z_3 + \check{\rho}_{14} z_4 + \check{w}_1 \\
y_2 &= \check{\pi}_{21} z_1 + \check{v}_2 & y_2 &= \check{\rho}_{21} z_1 + \check{\rho}_{22} z_2 + \check{\rho}_{23} z_3 + \check{\rho}_{24} z_4 + \check{w}_2
\end{aligned}
\tag{9-1}
$$

The right-hand set in (9-1) is necessary for estimating the first and useful for estimating the other equations of (8-1). Let us omit the bird ($\check{\ }$) where it is obvious.

Next, we compute the moments of the residuals on one another and construct two new matrices $\mathbf{D}(k)$ and $\mathbf{N}(k)$:

$$
\mathbf{D}(k) = \mathbf{m}_{(y_2, \ldots, y_{G^*}; z_1, \ldots, z_{H^*})(y_2, \ldots, y_{G^*}; z_1, \ldots, z_{H^*})}
$$
$$
- k \mathbf{m}_{(w_2, \ldots; w_{G^*}, 0, \ldots, 0)(w_2, \ldots, w_{G^*}; 0, \ldots, 0)}
$$
$$
\mathbf{N}(k) = \mathbf{m}_{(y_2, \ldots, y_{G^*}; z_1, \ldots, z_{H^*}) \cdot y_1} - k \mathbf{m}_{(w_2, \ldots, w_{G^*}; 0, \ldots, 0) \cdot w_1}
$$

where k is a variable that will be defined below. Then the estimates of the βs and γs of the first equation are given by

$$
\text{est } (\beta_2, \ldots, \beta_{G^*}, \gamma_1, \ldots, \gamma_{H^*}) = [\mathbf{D}(k)]^{-1} \mathbf{N}(k)
\tag{9-2}
$$

Theil has proved that, if $k = 0$, then (9-2) gives the naïve least squares estimate with y_1 treated as the sole dependent variable. If $k = 1$, (9-2) gives the method of unweighted instrumental variables of Sec. 7.7.   If $k = 1 + \nu$, where ν is the smallest root of

$$\det\left[\mathbf{m}_{(v_1, \ldots, v_{G^*})(v_1, \ldots v_{G^*})} - (1 + \nu)\mathbf{m}_{(w_1, \ldots, w_{G^*})(w_1, \ldots, w_{G^*})}\right] = 0 \quad (9\text{-}3)$$

then the estimates of (9-2) are identical with the limited information estimates of Chap. 8.   All these estimates except for the $k = 0$ case are consistent, but biased in the βs.   In the case $k = 1$, the bias itself can be estimated and corrected for.[1]

These findings not only are exciting for their beauty and symmetry, but are practical as well.   The regressions (9-1) are straightforward and attainable by simple calculation (see Appendix B) even for large systems.   The solution of (9-3) is not too hard, since the number G^* of present endogenous variables seldom exceeds 3 or 4 in any actual models.   But (9-3) must be calculated over again if we decide to estimate the second or third equation of the original model.   Theil states that his technique works if the remaining equations of the system are nonlinear and that it works for large samples even when some of the z's are lagged values of some y.

9.3. Treatment of models that are not exactly identified

This section gives advice on how to treat models that in their natural state contain some underidentified or some overidentified equations, or both.   The alternatives are listed from the most desirable to the least desirable, disregarding the cost of computation.

If a model contains some underidentified equations, we need do nothing about them unless we wish to estimate them.   The remaining equations, if identified, can be estimated in any case.

If we wish to estimate the underidentified equation, we must make certain alterations:

1. Make it identified by bringing in parameter estimates from independent sources, say, cross-section data.   There are pitfalls of a new kind in this method, however, which are noted briefly in Chap. 12.

2. Identify the equation in question by strategically adding variables elsewhere in the model.   This process, however, might de-identify the rest of the model.

3. Go ahead and estimate the underidentified equation; then, if you have *a priori* information on covariances, perform the tests of Sec. 6.9

---

[1] Compare with Appendix B.

to detect (or try to detect) whether you have estimated a bogus function.

If, on the other hand, the model contains some overidentified equations:

1. Use the full information, maximum likelihood method. This will yield consistent and efficient estimates of the identifiable parameters.

2. Use the limited information, maximum likelihood method.

3. Use instrumental variables, weighted.

4. Use instrumental variables, unweighted.

5. In the given equations, add variables where they are most relevant in such a way as to remove the overidentification.

6. Enlarge the system by endogenizing a previously exogenous variable.

7. In the original overidentified model, remove the overidentification by introducing redundant variables in the other equations. If it turns out that the redundant variable has a significant parameter, you have succeeded.

8. Drop variables to remove the overidentification. Instead of outright dropping, you may linearly combine two or more such variables. This cannot always be done, because the combined variables are not always present together or absent together elsewhere in the model.

9. Use the reduced form, and select arbitrarily one of the several sets of alternative estimates.

Underidentification is a more serious handicap than overidentification. To remove the former you *have* to make material alterations in the model. To remove the latter you can always use the full information method.

Whatever the final alterations, I would begin by constructing my models without worrying about identification. In doing so, I am sure that I am acting in the light of my best *a priori* wisdom, given the objectives of my study and my computing budget. If it turns out that identification makes alterations necessary, I think that honesty requires me to keep a record of the identifying alterations. Like Ariadne's thread, this record keeps track of my search for a second best; I may want to give up in frustration and return to try another way out of the Minotaur's chamber.

9.4. The "natural state" of an econometric model

Econometricians have devoted a good deal of attention to over-identified models. This entire book, from Chap. 6 on, is devoted to developing various approximations[1] to the full information method, which everybody tries to avoid because of its burdensome arithmetic. According to Liu,[2] we have been wasting our effort, because all well-conceived econometric models are in truth necessarily underidentified:

In economic reality, there are so many variables which have an important influence on the dependent variable in any structural equation that all structural relationships are likely to be "underidentified."

So Liu would not use any of our elaborate techniques, but would estimate just the reduced form and do so by simple least squares. The reduced form is to include as many exogenous variables as our knowledge and computational patience permit. Liu would then use these estimates for forecasting, and claims that they forecast better than all other techniques.

These subversive ideas deserve careful consideration. Is it true that structural equations in their natural, unemasculated, noble-savage state are underidentified? If they are, in what sense are forecasts from the reduced form better?

To begin with, there are occasions in which the investigator does not care to know the values of the structural parameters and is content with some kind of reduced form. To illustrate one occasion of this sort, assume that the investigator

1. Works from a typical and large enough sample
2. Forecasts for an economy of fixed structure
3. Forecasts from exogenous variables that stay in their sample ranges

Under the above conditions, an investigator would be glad to work with a ready-made reduced form though not necessarily with parameters estimated by simple least squares. He would accept the latter *if justifiable*, not for want of anything better.

---

[1] Unweighted and weighted instrumental variables and limited information.

[2] Ta-Chung Liu, "A Simple Forecasting Model for the U.S. Economy," p. 437 (*International Monetary Fund Staff Papers*, pp. 434–466, August, 1955).

Are econometric models necessarily underidentified? Admittedly, it is an oversimplification, as Liu states,[1] to impose the condition that certain variables be absent from a given structural equation. But it is gross "overcomplification"—to coin a much-needed word—to impose no condition at all, inviting into the demand for left-handed, square-headed $\frac{1}{8}$-inch bolts (and on equal *a priori* standing with the price of steel) the average diameter of tallow candles and the failure or success of the cod catch off the banks of Newfoundland. My instinct advises me to go halfway concerning these new variables: neither leave them out altogether nor admit them as equals. Consider the model

$$\begin{aligned} q + \alpha p + \gamma r + \delta f &= u \\ \beta q + p &= v \end{aligned} \qquad (9\text{-}4)$$

consisting of one underidentified and one overidentified equation. Now, if r and f are admitted as equals in the second equation, with parameters of their own, the whole system becomes underidentified. But the very knowledge that first convinced us to leave them out of the second equation now advises us to tack them on with *a priori small* parameters, small *relative* to β, γ, etc. A reasonable restatement might be the following:

$$\begin{aligned} q + \alpha p + \gamma r + \delta f &= u \\ \beta q + p + j\beta r + k\delta f &= v \end{aligned} \qquad (9\text{-}5)$$

where j, k are small constants, say $\frac{1}{1000}$, $\frac{1}{100}$, or some other not unreasonable value. And now (wonder of wonders!) both equations have become identified. The trick does not always work. For instance, it does not help in

$$\begin{aligned} q + \alpha p + \gamma r &= u_1 \\ \beta q + p &= u_2 \end{aligned} \qquad (9\text{-}6)$$

to fill the hole with $k\alpha r$, nor $k\beta r$, nor $k\gamma r$ because we still have *three* parameters (α, β, γ) to estimate and the reduced form contains only *two* coefficients $\tilde{\pi}_1 = m_{qr}/m_{rr}$, $\tilde{\pi}_2 = m_{pr}/m_{rr}$. However, if the supply of exogenous variables is less niggardly than in (9-6) it is not hard to find reasonable ways to complete a model so as to identify it in its entirety, if we so desire.

The most difficult and dangerous step is the assigning of values to

[1] *Ibid.*, p. 465.

j and k. The values must have the correct algebraic sign; otherwise, structural parameters are wildly misestimated. If the correct magnitudes for j and k are unknown, it is better to err on the small side than on the large. Too small (positive or negative) a value of j is better than a hole in the equation, but too large a value may be worse than a hole.

9.5. What are good forecasts?

If we want to forecast from an underidentified model, we have no choice but to use some kind of reduced form; from an overidentified model, it is *convenient*, not compulsory, to work from a reduced form. The entire question in both cases is: What sort of reduced form? How ought we to compute its coefficients?

To pin down our ideas, we shall consider the model $\mathbf{By} + \mathbf{\Gamma z} = \mathbf{u}$, where $\mathbf{u}$ has all the Simplifying Properties; in addition we shall make the covariances $\sigma_{u_g u_h}$ known fixed constants, possibly all equal, so as to keep them out of the way of the likelihood function. This way we concentrate attention on the *structural parameters* β, γ, and π and their rival estimates. The reduced form is $\mathbf{y} = \mathbf{\Pi z} + \mathbf{v}$, where $\mathbf{\Pi} = -\mathbf{B}^{-1}\mathbf{\Gamma}$, $\mathbf{v} = \mathbf{B}^{-1}\mathbf{u}$. The reduced form contains the entire set of exogenous variables whether the original form is exactly, over-, or underidentified.

Maximum likelihood minimizes

$$\sum_t \sum_g u_{gt}^2$$

by the βs and γs; limited information and instrumental variables approximate this. The naïve reduced form advocated by Liu minimizes

$$\sum_t \sum_g v_{gt}^2$$

by the πs (whatever these may be). Naturally, the two procedures are not equivalent, and, naturally, the second guarantees that residuals will be forecast with minimum variance.[1] But what is so good about forecasting *residuals* with minimum variance? The *forecasts themselves*

---

[1] Provided the sample and structure conform to conditions 1 to 3 of Sec. 9.4.

in both cases are (in general) biased, but the forecasts by maximum likelihood have the greater probability of being right.

In Fig. 18, p is the course of future events *if no disturbances occur*. The curve labeled $\hat{p}$ shows the (biased) probability distribution of the full information, maximum likelihood estimate of p; it is in general biased ($\varepsilon\hat{p} \neq p$) but has its peak at p itself. Curve $\tilde{p}$ is another maximum likelihood estimate (say, instrumental variables or limited information); it too has a peak at p but a lower one, perhaps a different bias $\varepsilon\tilde{p}$, and certainly a larger variance than $\hat{p}$. The reduced-form least squares estimate is distributed as in curve $\check{p}$; naturally it has a

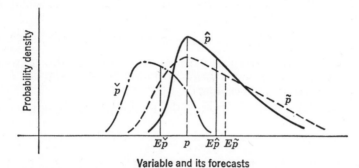

Variable and its forecasts

Fig. 18. The properties of forecasts. p: the true value of the forecast variable under zero disturbances. $\check{p}$: reduced-form least squares estimates. $\hat{p}$: full-information maximum likelihood estimates. $\tilde{p}$: other maximum likelihood estimates.

smaller spread than $\hat{p}$ and $\tilde{p}$; it may be more or less biased than either; but *its peak is off* p.

To put this into words: If, in the postsample year, all disturbances happen to be zero, maximum likelihood estimates forecast perfectly, and least squares forecast imperfectly. If the disturbances are non-zero, both forecast imperfectly; but, on the average and in the long run, least squares forecasts are less dispersed around their (biased) mean.

Which criterion is more reasonable is, I think, open to debate. I favor maximum likelihood estimates for much the same reason that I accept the maximum likelihood criterion in the first place: If we are to predict the future course of events, why not predict that the *most* probable thing ($u = 0$) will happen? What else can we sanely assume—the second most probable? On the other hand, if my job depends on the average success of my forecasts, I shall choose the least biased technique and disregard the highest probability of particular instances. If I want to make a showing of unswerving, unvacillating steadfastness, I shall use the least squares technique on the reduced form, even though it steadfastly throws my forecasts off the mark in each particular instance and in the totality of instances.

Further readings

The reference for Sec. 9.2 is H. Theil, "Estimation of Parameters of Econometric Models" (*Bulletin de l'institut international de statistique*, vol. 34, pt. 2, pp. 122–129, 1954). It is full of misprints.

Extraneous estimators are illustrated in KLEIN, chap. 5, where he pools time-series and cross-section data. Their statistical and common-sense difficulties are discussed in Edwin Kuh and John R. Meyer, "How Extraneous Are Extraneous Estimates?" (*Review of Economics and Statistics*, vol. 39, no. 4, pp. 380–393, November, 1957).

TINBERGEN, pp. 200–204, discusses the advantages and disadvantages of working from a reduced form, but overlooks that its least squares estimation is maximum likelihood only for an underidentified or exactly identified system.

Ever since Haavelmo, Koopmans, and others proposed elaborate methods for correct simultaneous estimation, naïve and not-so-naïve least squares has not lacked ardent defenders. Carl F. Christ, "Aggregate Econometric Models" [*American Economic Review*, vol. 46, no. 3, pp. 385–408 (especially in pp. 397–401), June, 1956], claims that least squares forecasts are likely to be more clustered than other forecasts; and Karl A. Fox, "Econometric Models of the U.S. Economy" (*Journal of Political Economy*, vol. 64, no. 2, pp. 128–142, April, 1956), has performed simple least squares regressions using the data and form of the Klein-Goldberger model (for reference, see Further Readings, chap. 1). See also Carl F. Christ, "A Test of an Econometric Model of the United States 1921–1947" (Universities–National Bureau Committee, *Conference on Business Cycles*, New York, pp. 35–107, 1951), with comments by Milton Friedman, Lawrence R. Klein, Geoffrey H. Moore, and Jan Tinbergen and a reply by Christ, pp. 107–129. In pp. 45–50 Christ summarizes the properties of rival estimating procedures. E. G. Bennion, in "The Cowles Commission's 'Simultaneous Equations Approach': A Simplified Explanation" (*Review of Economics and Statistics*, vol. 34, no. 1, pp. 49–56, 1952), illustrates why least squares gives a better historical relationship and better forecasts (as long as exogenous variables stay in their historical range) than do simultaneous estimates. John R. Meyer and Henry Laurence Miller, Jr., "Some Comments on the 'Simultaneous-equation

Approach'" (*Review of Economics and Statistics*, vol. 36, no. 1, February, 1954), state very clearly the different kinds of situations in which forecasts have to be made—and to each corresponds a proper estimating procedure.

Herman Wold says that he wrote *Demand Analysis* (New York: John Wiley & Sons, Inc., 1953) in large part to reinstate "a good many methods which have sometimes been declared obsolete, like the least squares regression or the short-cut of consumer units in the analysis of family budget data" and to "reveal and take advantage of the wealth of experience and common sense that is embodied in the familiar procedures of the traditional methods" (from page x of the preface). He believes that the economy is in truth *recursive* and that it can be described by recursive models whose equations, in the proper sequence, can be estimated by least squares. His second chapter, entitled "Least Squares under Debate" (especially secs. 7 to 9), is very far from convincing me that he is right.

CHAPTER 10

Searching for hypotheses and testing them

10.1. Introduction

Crudely stated, the subject of this chapter is how to tell whether some variables of a given set vary together or not and which ones do so more than others. The problem is how to make three interrelated choices: (1) a choice among the variables available, (2) a choice among the different ways they can vary together, and (3) a choice among different criteria for measuring the togetherness of their variation. The whole thing is like a complicated referendum for simultaneously (1) choosing the number and identity of the delegates, (2) deciding whether they should sit in a unicameral or multicameral legislature, and (3) supplying them with rules of procedure to use when they go into session.

This triple task is too much for a statistician, as it is for a citizenry: it wastes statistical data, as it wastes voters' time and attention. Just as, in practice, people settle independently, arbitrarily, and at a prior stage the number of chambers, the number of delegates, and the rules of procedure, so the statistician uses *maintained hypotheses.*

For example, in the model $C_t = \alpha + \gamma Z_t + u_t$ of Chap. 1, the presence of one and not two equations, two and not four variables, all the remaining stochastic and structural assumptions, and the requirement for maximizing likelihood are the maintained hypotheses. Only rival hypotheses about the true parameter values α and γ remain to be tested. The entire field of hypothesis searching and testing consists of variations on the above theme. The maintained hypotheses can be made more or less liberal, or they may change roles with the *questioned hypotheses*. Section 10.4 lists many specific examples.

The general moral of this chapter is this: Having used your data to accept or reject a hypothesis while maintaining others, you are not supposed to turn around, maintain your first decision, and test another hypothesis with the same data. If you are interested in testing two hypotheses from the same set of data, you must test them together. Thus, if you want to find both the form *and* personnel of government preferred by the French, you should ask them to rank on the ballot all combinations (like Gaillard/unicameral, Gaillard/bicameral, Pinay/unicameral, Pinay/bicameral) and to decide simultaneously who is to lead *and* which type of parliament; not the man first and the type second; not the type first and the man second.

Everything that follows in this chapter pretends that variables are measured without error. Sections 10.2 and 10.3 introduce two new concepts: discontinuous hypotheses and the null hypothesis. Sections 10.4 to 10.8 explore some of the commonest hypotheses considered by econometricians, especially when they set about to specify a model.

10.2. Discontinuous hypotheses

Consider again the simple model $C_t = \alpha + \gamma Z_t + u_t$. The rival hypotheses here are alternative values of α and γ and may be any pair of real numbers. This is an example of continuity.

Now consider this problem: Does x depend on y, or the other way around? Taking the dependence (for simplicity only) to be linear and homogeneous, the rival hypotheses here are

$$x_t = \gamma y_t + u_t \quad \text{versus} \quad y_t = \delta x_t + v_t$$

The answer is yes or no; either the first or the second equation holds. This is an example of discontinuity. However, the further problem of the size of γ (or δ), by itself, may be a continuous hypothesis problem.

Many of my examples below (Sec. 10.4) are discontinuous. The simple maximizing rules of the calculus do not work when there is discontinuity, and this fact makes it very interesting.

10.3. The null hypothesis

In selecting among hypotheses we can proceed in two ways: (1) compare them all to one another; (2) compare them each to a special, simple one, called the *null hypothesis* (symbolized by H_0). An example of the first procedure is the maximum likelihood estimation of (α,γ) in the model $C_t = \alpha + \gamma Z_t + u_t$, since it compares all conceivable pairs (α,γ) in choosing the most likely among them. The other way to proceed is somewhat as follows: select a null hypothesis, for example, $\alpha = 3$ and $\gamma = 0.7$, and accept or reject it (i.e., accept the proposition "either $\alpha \neq 3$ or $\gamma \neq 0.7$, or both") from evidence in the sample. I have more to say later on about how to select a null hypothesis and what criteria to use for accepting or rejecting it. Meanwhile, note that the decision to proceed via null hypothesis has nothing to do with continuity and discontinuity, though it happens that many applications of the null hypothesis technique are in discontinuous problems.

10.4. Examples of rival hypotheses

Many of the examples in this section are linear and homogeneous for the sake of simplicity only; in these cases linearity (and homogeneity) is guaranteed not to affect the principle discussed. In other examples, however, linearity (or homogeneity) is a rival hypothesis and thus very much involved in the principle discussed. Now to the examples:

1. Which one variable from a given set of explanatory variables is best? For instance, should we put income, past income, past consumption, or age in a rudimentary consumption function? The rival hypotheses here are

$$C_t = \beta Y_t + u_t \qquad C_t = \gamma Y_{t-1} + u_t \qquad C_t = \delta C_{t-1} + u_t \qquad \text{etc.}$$

2. Should the single term be linear or quadratic, logarithmic, etc.? The rival hypotheses here are

$$C_t = \beta Y_t + u_t \qquad C_t = \gamma Y_t^2 + u_t \qquad C_t = \delta \log Y_t + u_t \qquad \text{etc.}$$

Note that this becomes a special case of example 1 if we agree that Y^2, log Y, etc., are different variables from Y (Sec. 10.9).

3. What value of the single parameter is best? In $C_t = \beta Y_t + u_t$ the rival hypotheses are different values of β, say, $\beta = 1$, $\beta = \frac{1}{2}$, $\beta = \frac{3}{4}$, and others. This, too, is a special case of example 1, because it can be expressed as a choice among the explanatory variables Y, $2Y$, $4Y/3$, respectively.

4. Should there be one or more equations in the model? This question, important when several variables are involved, lurks behind the problems of confluence (see Sec. 6.14), but it arises even with two variables.

The above examples generalize, naturally. For instance, the question may be which two or which three variables to include, which linearly, which nonlinearly, how many lags, and how far back.

5. Which variables are to be regressed on which? The rival hypotheses are

$$x_1 = \alpha x_2 + u \quad \text{versus} \quad x_2 = \beta x_1 + v$$

for two variables. If we maintain the hypothesis of three variables in a single equation, the rival hypotheses are

$$x_1 = \alpha x_2 + \beta x_3 + u \quad \text{versus} \quad x_2 = \gamma x_1 + \delta x_3 + v$$
$$\text{versus} \quad x_3 = \epsilon x_1 + \zeta x_2 + w$$

And, if we maintain three variables and two equations, the rival hypotheses become

$$\begin{aligned} x_1 &= \alpha x_2 + \beta x_3 + u \\ x_2 &= \gamma x_1 + \delta x_3 + v \end{aligned} \quad \text{versus} \quad \begin{aligned} x_1 &= \epsilon x_2 + \zeta x_3 + w \\ x_3 &= \eta x_1 + \theta x_2 + t \end{aligned}$$
$$\text{versus} \quad \begin{aligned} x_2 &= \kappa x_1 + \lambda x_3 + s \\ x_3 &= \mu x_1 + \nu x_2 + r \end{aligned}$$

and so on for more equations and more variables. This is typically a discontinuous problem. It is discussed briefly in Sec. 10.8.

6. Having decided that x_1 is an explanatory variable, does it help

to include x_2 as well?   The rival hypotheses are

$$y = \alpha x_1 + v \quad \text{versus} \quad y = \beta x_1 + \gamma x_2 + w$$

Section 10.8 contains hints on this problem.

7. Having decided to include x_1, which one other variable should be added?

$$y = \alpha x_1 + \beta x_2 + u \quad \text{versus} \quad y = \gamma x_1 + \delta x_3 + v \qquad \text{etc.}$$

Section 10.8 applies to this problem.

8. Is it better to have a ratio model or an additive one?

$$\frac{c}{n} = \alpha \frac{y}{n} + u \quad \text{versus} \quad c = \beta y + \gamma n + v$$

This is discussed in Sec. 10.10.

9. Is it better to have a separate equation for each economic sector or the same equation to which is added a variable characterizing the sector?   For example, consider the following rival demand models:

$$\begin{aligned} q &= \alpha p + u \quad \text{for the poor} \\ q &= \beta p + v \quad \text{for the rich} \end{aligned} \quad \text{versus} \quad q = \gamma p + \delta y + w$$

where y is income.   Section 10.11 discusses this problem.

10. (A special case of the above.)   Are dummy variables better than separate equations?

$$q = \alpha p + u \quad \text{in wartime} \qquad\qquad q = \gamma p + \delta Q + w$$

versus

$$q = \beta p + v \quad \text{in peacetime} \qquad\qquad \begin{aligned} Q &= 0 \quad \text{in peacetime} \\ Q &= 1 \quad \text{in wartime} \end{aligned}$$

This problem is a special case of the example discussed in Sec. 10.11.

11. Do variables interact?   That is to say, does the *size* of one or more variables fortify (or nullify) the others' separate effects?   For instance, if being stupid and being old (the variables s and a, respectively) are bad for earning income, are stupidity and old age in combination worse than the sum of their separate effects?   The rival hypotheses are

$$y = \alpha s + \beta a + u \quad \text{versus} \quad y = \gamma s + \delta a + \epsilon s a + v$$

and can also be expressed as follows:

$$y = \gamma s + \delta a + \epsilon s a + v \qquad \text{Null hypothesis: } \epsilon = 0$$

or as follows:

$$y = \alpha s + \beta + u \text{ for the young}$$
$$y = \gamma s + \delta + v \text{ for the old} \qquad \text{Null hypothesis: } \begin{array}{l} \alpha = \gamma \\ \beta = \delta \end{array}$$

This case is not spelled out, but the discussion of Sec. 10.6 applies to it.

This list is not exhaustive. And, naturally, the above questions can be combined into complex hypotheses.

Digression on correlation and kindred concepts

This is a good place to gather together some definitions and theorems and to issue some simple but often unheeded warnings. It is also an excellent opportunity to learn, by doing the exercises, to manipulate correlations and regression coefficients as well as all sorts of moments.

Universe and sample. Keep in mind that Greek letters refer to properties of the universe and that Latin letters are used to refer to the corresponding sample properties.

Thus, as already explained in the Digression of Sec. 1.12, σ_{xx}, σ_{xy}, σ_{yy} are population variances and covariances of x and y. The corresponding sample quantities[1] are m_{xx}, m_{xy}, m_{yy}, the so-called "moments from the sample means," introduced in the same Digression,

$$m_{xy} = \sum_s (x_s - x^0)(y_s - y^0)$$

---

[1] To the population covariances σ_{xy} there correspond two types of sample quantities: those measured from the mean of the universe,

$$q_{xy} = \sum_s (x_s - \varepsilon x)(y_s - \varepsilon y)$$

where s runs over the sample S^0; and those measured from the mean of the sample, namely m_{xy}. Interchanging q_{xy} and m_{xy} does not hurt at all, in general, when the underlying model is linear, since m_{xy} is an unbiased, consistent, etc., estimator of both q_{xy} and σ_{xy}, etc. There are difficulties in the case of nonlinear models, but we shall not go into them here.

where s runs over the sample S^0. The *universe coefficient of correlation* ρ is defined by

$$\rho_{xy}^2 = \frac{(\sigma_{xy})^2}{\sigma_{xx}\sigma_{yy}}$$

and the corresponding *sample coefficient* r by

$$r_{xy}^2 = \frac{(m_{xy})^2}{m_{xx}m_{yy}}$$

Later on we define partial, multiple, etc., coefficients of correlation. In all cases, a coefficient of correlation measures the togetherness of *two and only two variables*, though one or both may be compounded of several others. This elementary fact is often forgotten.

For the sake of symmetry in notation, when handling several variables, we shall use x with subscripts: x_1, x_2, x_3, etc. Then we write simply ρ_{12}, r_{12}, m_{12} for $\rho_{(x_1)(x_2)}$, $r_{(x_1)(x_2)}$, $m_{(x_1)(x_2)}$, etc.

Both ρ_{xy} and r_{xy} range from -1 to $+1$. Values very near ± 1 mean that x and y have a tight *linear* fit like $\alpha x + \beta y = u$, with the residuals very small. A tight nonlinear fit like $x^2 + y^2 = 1$ does not yield a large coefficient of correlation ρ_{xy}. What we need to describe this fit is $\rho_{(x^2)(y^2)}$. And similarly for relations like $\alpha y + \beta \log x = u$ or $\alpha y^2 + \beta x^3 = u$, we need $\rho_{(\log x)(y)}$, $\rho_{(x^3)(y^2)}$, respectively.

10.5. Linear confluence

From now on until the contrary is stated, I shall deal with linear relations exclusively. The discussion is perfectly general for any finite number of variables, but three are enough to capture the essence of the problems with which we shall be dealing. Let the three variables be

X_1 number of pints of liquor sold at a ski resort in a day
X_2 number of tourists present in the resort area
X_3 average daily temperature

We suppose there are one or several linear stochastic relationships among some or all of these variables. The least-squares-regression coefficients are denoted by a's and b's, with a standard system of subscripts.

Begin with regressions among X_1, X_2, X_3, taken two at a time; there are six such regressions. In (10-1) below these regressions are arranged in rows according to the variable that is treated as if it were dependent and in columns according to the variable treated as independent.

$$\cdot\cdot\cdot\cdot\cdot\cdot\cdot\cdot\cdot\cdot \qquad X_1 = a_{1\cdot2} + b_{12}X_2 \qquad X_1 = a_{1\cdot3} + b_{13}X_3$$
$$X_2 = a_{2\cdot1} + b_{21}X_1 \qquad \cdot\cdot\cdot\cdot\cdot\cdot\cdot\cdot\cdot\cdot \qquad X_2 = a_{2\cdot3} + b_{23}X_3 \quad (10\text{-}1)$$
$$X_3 = a_{3\cdot1} + b_{31}X_1 \qquad X_3 = a_{3\cdot2} + b_{32}X_2 \qquad \cdot\cdot\cdot\cdot\cdot\cdot\cdot\cdot\cdot\cdot$$

In each subscript, the very first digit denotes the dependent variable. If there is a second digit before any dot appears, it denotes the independent variable to which the coefficient belongs. Digits after the dot (if any) represent the other independent variables (if any) present elsewhere in the equation. The order of digits *before* the dot is material, because it tells which variable is regressed on which. The order of subscripts *after* the dot is immaterial, because these digits merely record the other "independent" variables.

The same three variables can be regressed three at a time. There are three such regressions:

$$X_1 = a_{1\cdot23} + b_{12\cdot3}X_2 + b_{13\cdot2}X_3$$
$$X_2 = a_{2\cdot13} + b_{21\cdot3}X_1 + b_{23\cdot1}X_3 \qquad (10\text{-}2)$$
$$X_3 = a_{3\cdot12} + b_{31\cdot2}X_1 + b_{32\cdot1}X_2$$

As an exercise, consider the four-variable regression

$$X_1 = a_{1\cdot234} + b_{12\cdot34}X_2 + b_{13\cdot24}X_3 + b_{14\cdot23}X_4$$

and fill in the missing subscripts in

$$X_3 = a_{\_\cdot\_\_} + b_{\_\_\cdot\_}X_1 + b_{\_\_\cdot\_}X_2 + b_{\_\_\cdot\_}X_4$$

Returning to our liquor example, suppose we decide to measure the three variables not from zero but from each one's sample mean. If primed small letters represent the transformed variables, we know that the a's drop out and the b's remain unchanged. This is so because the model is linear. Our relations (10-1) and (10-2) now become

$$x_1' = b_{12}x_2' \qquad \cdots \qquad x_3' = b_{31\cdot2}x_1' + b_{32\cdot1}x_2'$$

Exercises

10.A   Prove $r_{(X_1)(X_2)} = r_{(x_1')(x_2')} = r_{12}$, that is to say, that correlation does not depend on the origin of measurement.

10.B   Prove

$$r_{ij}^2 = b_{ij}b_{ji}$$

Hint: Use moments.

This relation says that the coefficient of correlation between two variables equals the geometric mean of the two regression slopes we get if we treat each in turn as the independent variable.   The less these two regressions differ, the nearer is the correlation to $+1$ or -1.

10.6. Partial correlation

Two factors may account for x_1', the sale of a lot of liquor: (1) there are many people (x_2'); (2) it is very cold (x_3').   This relation is expressed

$$x_1' = b_{12 \cdot 3}x_2' + b_{13 \cdot 2}x_3' \tag{10-3}$$

But the reason that (1) there are many people in the resort is (a) that the weather is cold, and (possibly) (b) that a lot of drinking is going on there, making it fun to be there apart from the pleasure of skiing. This is expressed

$$x_2' = b_{21 \cdot 3}x_1' + b_{23 \cdot 1}x_3' \tag{10-4}$$

Suppose we wanted to know whether liquor sales would be correlated with crowds in the absence of weather variations.   The measure we seek is the *partial correlation between x_1' and x_2', allowing for x_3'.*   This measure is symbolized by $r_{12 \cdot 3}$.   It is interpreted as follows:

Define the variables

$$y_1' = x_1' - b_{13 \cdot 2}x_3' \tag{10-5}$$
$$y_2' = x_2' - b_{23 \cdot 1}x_3' \tag{10-6}$$

The y's are sales corrected for weather only and tourists corrected for weather only.   If we have corrected both for weather, any remaining covariation between them is due to (1) the normal desire for people to drink liquor (the more tourists the more liquor is sold), (2) the possibility that some tourists come to enjoy drinking rather than skiing (the more liquor, the more tourists), and (3) a combination of the first two items.

The partial coefficient of correlation is defined by

$$r_{12\cdot3} = r_{(y_1')(y_2')} \tag{10-7}$$

Exercises

10.C Prove $r_{21\cdot3} = r_{12\cdot3}$.

10.D Prove $r_{12\cdot3}^2 = b_{12\cdot3}b_{21\cdot3}$. This is analogous to Exercise 10.B. *Hint:* Substitute (10-6) and (10-7) into (10-3) and (10-4).

10.E Prove

$$r_{12\cdot3} = \frac{r_{12} - r_{13}r_{23}}{(1 - r_{13}^2)^{1/2}(1 - r_{23}^2)^{1/2}}$$

from definition (10-7) and Exercises 10.C and 10.D.

10.F Give a common sense interpretation of the propositions in the above three exercises.

10.G All this generalizes to four and more variables, but notation gets very messy. Exercise 10.D generalizes into the proposition: Every (partial or otherwise) coefficient of correlation equals the geometric mean of the two *relevant* regression coefficients. So, for example, $r_{12\cdot34}^2 = b_{12\cdot34}b_{21\cdot34}$.

Let **r** stand for the matrix of all simple coefficients of correlation r_{ij}, and let R_{ij} stand for the minor of r_{ij}. Then Exercise 10.E is rewritten

$$r_{12\cdot3}^2 = \frac{R_{12}^2}{R_{11}R_{22}}$$

and with four variables

$$r_{12\cdot34}^2 = r_{21\cdot34}^2 = r_{12\cdot43}^2 = r_{21\cdot43}^2 = \frac{R_{12}^2}{R_{11}R_{12}}$$

and so on for any number of variables, the dimension of R growing all the while, of course.

10.H Show that $r_{12\cdot3}^2 = R_{12}^2/R_{11}R_{22}$ holds but collapses into an identity when there is no third variable.

10.7. Standardized variables

Let us now measure X_1, X_2, X_3 not only as departures x_1', x_2', x_3' from their sample means but also in units equal to the sample standard deviation of each. So transformed, the variables are called just x_1, x_2, x_3.

$$x_i = \frac{x_i'}{\sqrt{m_{x_i x_i}}}$$

This step is useful in bunch map analysis (see Sec. 10.8). When this is done, nothing happens to either the population or the sample correlation coefficients, but the regression parameters between the variables do change.

Exercises

10.I Prove $m_{x_1 x_2} = (m_{x_1 x_1} m_{x_2 x_2})^{-\frac{1}{2}} m_{(x_1')(x_2')}$.

10.J Prove that $r_{(x_1')(x_2')} = r_{(x_1)(x_2)} = r_{12}$ by using Exercises 10.B and 10.C.

10.K Denote the regression coefficients among x_1', x_2', x_3' by the letter b and the corresponding coefficients among the standardized variables x_1, x_2, x_3 by the letter a, with appropriate subscripts. Interpret $a_{12 \cdot 3}$, $a_{21 \cdot 3}$, $a_{31 \cdot 2}$; show that they differ in meaning from $a_{1 \cdot 23}$, $a_{2 \cdot 13}$, $a_{3 \cdot 12}$, respectively.

10.L Show that $a_{12} = b_{12}(m_{22}/m_{11})^{\frac{1}{2}}$, and, in general, that $a_{ij \cdot k} = b_{ij \cdot k}(m_{jj}/m_{ii})^{\frac{1}{2}}$.

10.M Show, by using Exercise 10.L, that $r_{ij \cdot k}^2 = a_{ij \cdot k} a_{ji \cdot k}$.

10.N Show that $r_{12} = a_{12}$. This is a very important property, which says that regression and correlation coefficients are identical for standardized variables.

10.O Let $x_i'' = (X_i - \varepsilon X_i)(\sigma_{ii})^{-\frac{1}{2}}$. Prove $\rho_{(x_i'')(x_j'')} = \rho_{(X_i)(X_j)}$, and interpret.

10.8. Bunch map analysis

Bunch maps are mainly of archaeological or antiquarian interest. They seem to have gone out of fashion. BEACH (pp. 172–175) gives an excellent account of them which I shall not repeat here. I shall merely discuss necessary and sufficient conditions under which bunch maps help to accept or reject hypotheses.

Turn to the example of liquor sales, skiers, and cold weather in Sec. 10.5. Let x_1, x_2, x_3 be the three standardized variables. Let their correlation coefficients be

$$\mathbf{r} = \begin{bmatrix} 1 & r_{12} & r_{13} \\ r_{21} & 1 & r_{23} \\ r_{31} & r_{32} & 1 \end{bmatrix} = \begin{bmatrix} 1 & 0.5 & 0.2 \\ 0.5 & 1 & 0.8 \\ 0.2 & 0.8 & 1 \end{bmatrix}$$

Compute the least squares regressions of all normalized variables, two at a time:

$$\begin{array}{ccc}
\cdots\cdots & x_1 = a_{12}x_2 & x_1 = a_{13}x_3 \\
x_2 = a_{21}x_1 & \cdots\cdots & x_2 = a_{23}x_3 \\
x_3 = a_{31}x_1 & x_3 = a_{32}x_2 & \cdots\cdots
\end{array} \qquad (10\text{-}8)$$

and then three at a time:

$$\begin{aligned}
x_1 &= a_{12\cdot3}x_2 + a_{13\cdot2}x_3 \\
x_2 &= a_{21\cdot3}x_1 + a_{23\cdot1}x_3 \\
x_3 &= a_{31\cdot2}x_1 + a_{32\cdot1}x_2
\end{aligned} \qquad (10\text{-}9)$$

Construct now the unit squares, shown in Fig. 19, where 0 marks the origin. In each block the horizontal axis corresponds to the independent variable, and the vertical to the dependent. The labels below the squares show which is which.

Refer now to the first equation $x_1 = a_{12}x_2$ in (10-8). From Exercise 10.N, $x_1 = r_{12}x_2$. Imagine a unit variation in the independent variable x_2; then the corresponding variation in x_1, according to this equation, is a_{12}. Plot the point $(1, a_{12})$ in the first block of squares. Then go to the symmetrical equation $x_2 = a_{21}x_1$, make x_1 vary by $\Delta x_1 = 1$, and plot the resulting point $(a_{21}, 1)$ in the same block. In a similar way fill out the top row of Fig. 19, drawing the beams from the origin.

In (10-9), first consider the variation in x_1 resulting from variations in x_2, other things being equal. We get three different answers from (10-9), one per equation:

$$\begin{aligned}
\Delta x_1 &= a_{12\cdot3}\,\Delta x_2 \\
\Delta x_1 &= \frac{1}{a_{21\cdot3}}\,\Delta x_2 \\
\Delta x_1 &= -\frac{a_{32\cdot1}}{a_{31\cdot2}}\,\Delta x_2
\end{aligned} \qquad (10\text{-}10)$$

Digressing a little, I state without proof that

$$a_{ij\cdot k} = \frac{R_{ij}}{R_{ii}}$$

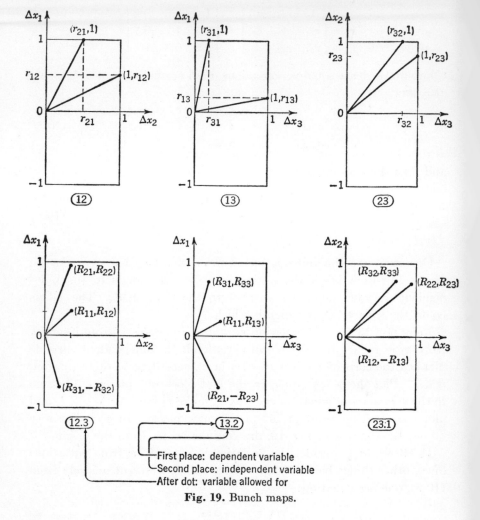

Fig. 19. Bunch maps.

Therefore we get from (10-10) the three statements that $\Delta x_1 : \Delta x_2$ is proportional to $R_{12} : R_{11}$, to $R_{22} : R_{21}$, and to $-R_{32} : R_{31}$. In the figure this is depicted, respectively, by the beams marked (12.3). The three regressions in general conflict both with regard to the *slope* and with regard to the *length* of the beams.

Derive the corresponding relations for $\Delta x_1 : \Delta x_3$ and $\Delta x_2 : \Delta x_3$. These results are plotted in the last two panels of Fig. 19.

Exercise

10.P   Plot the bunch maps for

$$\mathbf{r} = \begin{bmatrix} 1 & -0.6 & -0.1 \\ -0.6 & 1 & 0.6 \\ -0.1 & 0.6 & 1 \end{bmatrix}$$

Scanning Fig. 19 is supposed to tell us (1) which two variables to regress if we want to stick to two of the given three, and (2) whether a third variable is superfluous, useful, or detrimental in some very loose sense.

What do we look for in Fig. 19? Three things: (1) opening or closing of bunch maps as you go from the upper to the lower panel, (2) shortening of the beams, and (3) change of direction of the bunches. There is no simple intuitive way to interpret the many combinations of 1, 2, and 3; this is the main reason why statisticians have abandoned bunch maps.

The examples that follow far from exhaust the possibilities. The moral of these examples is: To interpret the behavior of the bunch maps, you must translate them into correlation coefficients r_{ij} and try to interpret what it means for the coefficients to be related in one way or another. But one might as well start with the correlation coefficients, bypassing the bunch maps altogether.

Example 1.   *The vanishing beam*

What can we infer if beam R_{12}/R_{11} shrinks in length? Take the extreme case $R_{12} = 0$ and $R_{11} = 0$. These imply $r_{12} = r_{23}r_{31}$ and $r_{23}^2 = 1$, which, in turn, imply $r_{23} = \pm 1$ and $r_{12} = \pm r_{13}$. Let us restrict the illustration to the plus-sign case $r_{23} = 1$, $r_{12} = r_{13}$.

The meaning of $r_{23} = 1$ is that x_2 and x_3 in the sample, uncorrected for variations in x_1, are indistinguishable variables. Relation $r_{12} = r_{13}$ shows that, if x_2 and x_3 were corrected for x_1, the corrections would be identical; the resulting corrected variables are also identical. This can also be seen from the fact that in these circumstances $r_{23 \cdot 1}$ equals 1. All this would, of course, be detectable from the top level of Fig. 19, signifying that three variables are too many and that any two are nearly as good as any other two.

Example 2. The tilting beam

What does it mean if beam R_{12}/R_{11} tilts toward one axis without shrinking in length? For instance, let $R_{12} \neq 0$ and $R_{11} = 0$. This implies again that $r_{23} = \pm 1$, that is to say, $x_2 = \pm x_3$. Taking again just the $+$ case, this signifies that the uncorrected x_2 and x_3 are in perfect agreement. However, $R_{12} = r_{12} - r_{13} \neq 0$ or $r_{12} \neq r_{13}$; take the case $r_{12} < r_{13}$ for the sake of the illustration. The inequality $r_{12} \neq r_{13}$ suggests that the corrections of x_2 and x_3 to take account of variations in x_1 will be *different* corrections and will upset the perfect harmony. This can be seen again from

$$r_{23 \cdot 1} = \frac{R_{23}}{(R_{22}R_{33})^{\frac{1}{2}}} = \frac{r_{23} - r_{12}r_{13}}{(1 - r_{13}^2)^{\frac{1}{2}}(1 - r_{12}^2)^{\frac{1}{2}}} = \frac{1 - r_{12}r_{13}}{(1 - r_{13}^2)^{\frac{1}{2}}(1 - r_{12}^2)^{\frac{1}{2}}} \neq 1$$

In terms of our example, there is a spurious perfect correlation between x_2, the number of skiers, and x_3, the weather. It is spurious because some skiers come to enjoy not the weather but the liquor. However, liquor sales respond less perfectly to tourist numbers than to weather; that is, $r_{12} < r_{13}$. Therefore, if you take into account the fact that liquor too attracts skiers, the weather is not so perfectly predictable a magnet for skiers as you might have thought by looking at $r_{23} = 1$. The hypothesis accepted in this case is: Liquor is significant and ought to be introduced in a predictive model.

Exercises

10.Q Show that, if beam $a_{12 \cdot 3}$ has the same slope as a_{12}, this implies $a_{12 \cdot 3} = r_{12}$ and also $r_{13} = r_{23}$ and, hence, that all three beams of the bunch map come together. Interpret this.

10.R Interpret the situation where all three beams R_{12}/R_{11}, R_{22}/R_{21}, and $-R_{32}/R_{31}$ have the same slope. Must they necessarily have the same length? Must the common slope necessarily equal a_{12}?

10.9. Testing for linearity

If the rival hypotheses are

$$y = \beta x + u \quad \text{versus} \quad y = \gamma x^2 + v$$

the matter is quickly settled by comparing the correlation coefficients r_{xy} with $r_{x^2 \cdot y}$. Things become complicated if the quadratic function contains a linear term, because the function $y = \gamma x^2 + \delta x + v$ contains the linear function $y = \beta x + u$ as a special case; therefore, we would expect the correlation to be improved by adding a higher term. Thus, for any fit giving estimates $\tilde{\beta}$, $\tilde{\gamma}$, and $\tilde{\delta}$, $r_{y \cdot (\tilde{\gamma} x^2 + \tilde{\delta} x)}$ is bound to be greater than $r_{y \cdot (\tilde{\beta} x)}$. Correlation coefficients do not give the best tests of linearity. Common sense suggests something simpler and more intuitive.

The curves in Fig. 20a represent the two rival hypotheses. If the

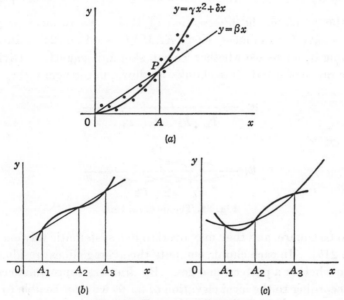

Fig. 20. Tests of nonlinearity.

quadratic is true but we fit a straight line, then the computed residuals from the fitted straight line will be overwhelmingly positive for some ranges of x and overwhelmingly negative for other ranges. These ranges are defined in terms of the intersections of the rival curves. Somewhere left of A most residuals are negative, and to the right, most are positive. Complicated numerical formulas for testing nonlinearity are nothing but algebraic translations of this simple test.

All this generalizes quite readily. For instance, the test of hypothesis $y = \alpha x + u$ versus a cubic is sketched in Fig. 20b; a quadratic versus a cubic in Fig. 20c. And it generalizes into several variables x, y, z, etc.

In each case the test consists in dividing the range of x into several equal parts $P_1, P_2, \ldots$, as shown in either Fig. 21a or 21b. In each part compute the average straight-line regression residual av $\check{u}$. If this tends to vary systematically (with a trend or in waves), the relationship is nonlinear.

When we have three or more variables x, y, z and want to test linearity versus some other hypothesis, we have to extend to two dimensions the technique of Fig. 21. Let the rival hypotheses be

$$x = \alpha + \beta y + \gamma z + u \quad \text{versus} \quad x = \delta + \epsilon y + \zeta y^2 + \eta z + \theta z^2 + \kappa yz + v$$

In the yz plane the intersection of these two surfaces projects a hard-to-solve-for and messy curve $KLMNP$ (see Fig. 22a). Instead of obtaining it, let us see whether we can sketch it vaguely. Divide the sample range of y and z into chunks, as shown in the figure (they do not

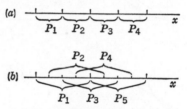

Fig. 21. The interval test.

need to be square, and they may overlap in a systematic way analogous to Fig. 21b). In each chunk, compute the average linear residual av $\check{u}$, and see whether a pattern emerges. By drawing approximate contour lines according to the local elevation of av $\check{u}$, we may be able to detect mountains or valleys, which tell us that the true relationship is nonlinear. Something analogous can be done when both rival hypotheses are nonlinear.

10.10. Linear versus ratio models

The rival hypotheses here are

$$\frac{c}{n} = \alpha + \beta \frac{y}{n} + u \quad \text{versus} \quad c = \gamma + \delta y + \epsilon n + v$$

where u and v have the usual properties to ensure that least squares fits are valid.

If the ratio model is the maintained hypothesis, then we would expect av $\check{u}$ to be constant over successive segments of the axis y/n. Translated into the projection on the yn plane, this means that av $\check{u}$ should be constant in the successive slices shown in Fig. 22b.   For the linear model, av $\check{v}$ should be constant in the squares of Fig. 22c.   In general, one criterion will be satisfied better than the other and will plead for the rejection of the opposite hypothesis.   If both criteria are

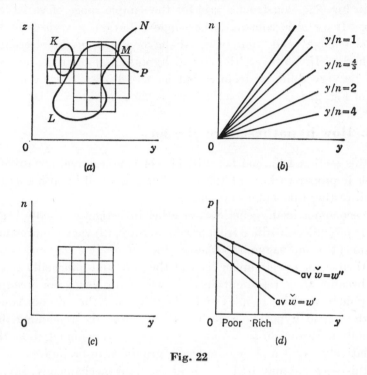

Fig. 22

substantially satisfied, then there is no problem of choosing, because both formulations say that c, y, and n are related linearly and homogeneously ($\gamma = 0$).   One formulation might possibly be more efficient than the other for reasons of "skedasticity" (compare Sec. 2.15).

10.11. Split sectors versus sector variable

The rival hypotheses here are whether the demand for, say, sugar should be estimated for all consumers as a linear function of price and income $q = \gamma p + \delta y + w$ (where the price paid is uncorrelated with income) or should be split into several demand functions $q = \alpha p + u$, $q = \beta p + v$, etc., one for each income class, on the ground that price means more to the poor than to the rich.

For illustration it is enough if we have just two income classes, the rich and the poor, corresponding to, say, $y = 10$, $y = 1$. Nothing essential would be added if y were taken as a continuous variable.

As in Fig. 22c, construct a grid for the sample range of variables y and p. If av w is constant, the single equation $q = \gamma p + \delta y + w$ is good enough, and, moreover, we have $\alpha = \beta$ in the alternative hypothesis. If, however, the second hypothesis is correct, not only will $\check{\alpha}$ be very different from $\check{\beta}$, but av $\check{w}$ will display contours like those of Fig. 22d.

10.12. How hypotheses are chosen

In this section I am neither critical, nor constructive, nor original. I think it proper to look at the way that statistical hypothesis making and testing takes place around us.

The econometrician, geneticist, or other investigator usually begins with (1) prejudices instilled from previous study, (2) vague impressions, (3) data, (4) some vague hypotheses.

He then casts a preliminary look at the data and informally rejects some because they represent special cases (war years, for instance, or extremely wealthy people) and others because they do not square with the vague hypotheses he holds. He uses the remaining data informally to throw out some of his hypotheses, from among those that are relatively vague and not too firmly grounded in prejudice.

At this stage he may prefer to scan the data mechanically, say, by bunch maps, rather than impressionistically. Mechanical prescreening is used (1) because the variables are many, and the unaided eye is bewildered by them, and (2) because the research worker is chicken-hearted and distrusts his judgment. Logically, of course, any mechanical method is an implicit blend of theory and estimating criteria; but, psychologically, it has the appearance of objectivity. The good researcher knows this, but he too is overwhelmed by the illusion that mechanisms are objective.

Having done all this, the investigator at long last comes to specification (as described in Chap. 1); he then estimates, accepts, rejects, or samples again.

This stage-by-stage procedure is logically wrong, but economically efficient, psychologically appealing, and practically harmless in the hands of a skilled researcher with a feel for his area of study.

Instead of proceeding stage by stage, is there a way to let the facts speak for themselves in one grand test?   The answer is no.   We must start with some hypothesis or we do not even have facts.   True, hypotheses may be more or less restrictive.   But the less restrictive the hypotheses are, the less a given body of data can tell us.

Further readings

For rigorous treatment of the theory of hypothesis testing, one needs to know set theory and topology.   KLEIN's discussion, pp. 56–62, gives a good first glimpse of this approach and a good bibliography, p. 63.

For treatment of errors in the variables, consult Trygve Haavelmo, "Some Remarks on Frisch's Confluence Analysis and Its Use in Econometrics," chap. V in KOOPMANS, pp. 258–265.

BEACH discusses bunch maps and the question of superfluous, useful, or detrimental variables, pp. 174–175.   TINBERGEN, pp. 80–83, shows a five-variable example.

Cyril H. Goulden, *Methods of Statistical Analysis*, 2d ed., chap. 7 (New York: John Wiley & Sons, Inc., 1952), gives an elementary discussion of ρ and the sample properties of its estimate r.

Unspecified factors

11.1. Reasons for unspecified factor analysis

Having specified his explanatory variables, the model builder frequently knows (or suspects) that there are other variables at work that are hard to incorporate.

1. The additional variable (or variables) may be unknown, like the planet Neptune, which used to upset other orbits.

2. The additional variable may be known but hard to measure. For instance, technological change affects the production function, but how are we to introduce it explicitly?

There are two ways out of this difficulty: splitting the sample, and dummy variables. When we split the sample we fit the production function to each fragment independently in the hope that each fragment is uniform enough with regard to the state of technology and yet large enough to contain sufficient degrees of freedom to estimate the parameters. The technique of dummy variables does not split the sample, but instead introduces a variable that takes on two and only two values or *levels*: 0 when, say, there is peace, and 1 when there is war. Phenomena that are capable of taking on three or more distinct states are not suited to the dummy variable technique. For instance, it

156

would not do to count 0 for peace, 0.67 for cold war, and 1 for shooting war, because this would impose an artificial metric scale on the state of world politics which would affect the parameters attached to honest-to-goodness, truly measurable variables. No artificial metric scale is introduced by the two-level dummy variable.

3. The additional factors at work may be a composite of many factors, too many to include separately and yet not numerous enough or independent enough of one another to relegate to the random term of the equation.

4. The additional variable may be known and measurable, but we may not know whether to include it linearly, quadratically, or otherwise.

5. The additional variable may be known, measurable, etc., but not simple to put in. To admit a wavy trend line, for instance, eats up several degrees of freedom.

In such cases the unspecified variable technique comes to our rescue, at a price, because it sometimes requires special knowledge. In the illustration of Sec. 11.2, for instance, to estimate a production function that shifts with technological change, time series are not enough. The data must contain information about inputs and outputs broken down, say, by region, or in some dimension besides chronology.

11.2. A single unspecified variable

This section is based on the technique developed by C. E. V. Leser[1] in his study of British coal mining during 1943–1953, years of rapid technological change, nationalization, and other disturbances.

He fitted the function $P_{rt} = g_t L_{rt}^\alpha C_{rt}^\beta$, where P is product, L is labor, C is capital, g_t is the unspecified impact of technology, r and t are regional and time indices, and α, β are the unknown parameters.

Here for exposition's sake, I shall linearize his model and drop the second specified variable. Consider then

$$P_{rt} = g_t + \alpha L_{rt} + u_{rt} \tag{11-1}$$

[1] C. E. V. Leser, "Production Functions and British Coal Mining" (*Econometrica*, vol. 23, no. 4, pp. 442–446, October, 1955).

The following assumptions are made:

1. Technology affects all regions equally in any moment of time.
2. The same production function applies to all regions.
3. The random term is normal, with a period mean

$$\frac{\sum_{r=1}^{R} u_{rt}}{R}$$

equal to zero, and a regional mean

$$\frac{\sum_{t=1}^{T} u_{rt}}{T}$$

also equal to zero. We shall now use the notation $av[r]u_{rt}$ and $av[t]u_{rt}$ for expressions like the last two.[1]

Now, keeping time fixed at $t_1 = 1$, let us average inputs and outputs over the R regions. From (11-1) we get, remembering that $av[r]g_{t_1} = g_{t_1}$,

$$av[r]P_{rt_1} = g_{t_1} + \alpha \, av[r]L_{rt_1} \tag{11-2}$$

And, by subtracting (11-2) from (11-1), we get the following relation between P'_{rt_1} and L'_{rt_1}, which are product and labor measured from their mean values of period 1:

$$P'_{rt_1} = \alpha L'_{rt_1} + u_{rt_1} \tag{11-3}$$

Do the same for $t = 2, \ldots, T$ and then maximize the likelihood of the sample. Under the usual assumptions, this is equivalent to minimizing the sum of squares

$$\sum_{rt} (u_{rt})^2$$

The resulting estimate of α is

$$\hat{\alpha} = \frac{m_{P'L'}}{m_{L'L'}} \tag{11-4}$$

In this expression the moments are sums running over all regions and time periods.

[1] Read "average over the r regions," "average over the t years."

Having found α, we can go back to (11-2) to compute the time path g_t of the unspecified variable, technology.

The method I have just outlined has several advantages:

1. It uses $R \times T$ observations (a large number of degrees of freedom) in estimating the parameter α.

2. Unlike split sampling, it obtains a single parameter estimate for all regions and periods.

3. It yields us an estimate of the unspecified variable (technological change), if it is the only other factor at work.

4. This technological change does not have to be a simple function of time. It may be secular, cyclical, or erratic; it can be linear, quadratic, or anything else.

5. The method estimates, in addition to technology, the effects of any number of other unspecified variables (such as inflation, war, nationalization) which at any moment may affect all regions equally.

The chief disadvantage of the technique is that the unspecified variable g_t has to be introduced in a manner congenial to the model, that is to say, as a linear term in a linear model, as a factor in Leser's logarithmic model, and so forth; otherwise it would not drop out, as in (11-3) when we express the specified variables as departures from their average values.

For the unspecified variable technique to be successful it is necessary that the data come classified in *one more dimension* than there are unspecified variables. Thus P and L must have two subscripts. Moreover, each region must have coal mines in each time period.[1]

11.3. Several unspecified variables

Imagine now that we wish to explain retail price P in terms of unit cost C, distance or location D, monopoly M, and the general level of inflation J. Cost is the specified variable, and location, monopoly, and inflation are left unspecified for one or another of the reasons I

---

[1] There are methods for treating *lacunes*, or missing data, but these are rather elaborate and will not be discussed in this work. The usual way to treat a lacune is by pretending it is full of data that interpolate perfectly in whatever structural relationship is finally assigned to the original data.

recounted in Sec. 11.1.   The model, assumed to be linear, is

$$P_{firt} = M_i + D_r + J_t + \alpha C_{firt} + u_{firt} \tag{11-5}$$

where the subscripts f, i, r, t express firm, industry, region, and time. The model, as written, maintains that the degree of monopoly is a property of the industry only, not of the region or of inflationary situation or of interactions among the three.   Similarly, inflation is solely a function of the time and not of the degree of monopoly and location of industry.   Note again that the data have to come classified in *one more dimension* than there are unspecified variables.   Thus P and C must have four subscripts, one for each of the unspecified variables, plus an extra one (firm f).   Moreover, unless we have lacunes, each firm must be present in each industry, region, and time period.   The firms of Montgomery Ward and Sears Roebuck would do,[1] and the industries they enter can be, say, watch retailing, tire retailing, clothing retailing, etc.

In that case, α is estimated analogously to (11-4) by $\hat{\alpha} = m_{P'C'}/m_{C'C'}$, where the moments are sums running over f, i, r, t.   Having estimated α, we can now define a new variable S, the price-cost spread $S = P - \hat{\alpha}C$.   The model is now

$$S_{firt} = M_i + D_r + J_t + v_{firt} \tag{11-6}$$

Estimating M, D, and J is the so-called *problem of linear factor analysis*.

11.4. Linear orthogonal factor analysis

Linear factor analysis attempts to explain the spread S as an additive resultant of two or more separate factors; in the example of (11-6) there are three factors: monopoly, region, and inflation.

Nothing essential is lost if we confine ourselves to two factors, say, monopoly and inflation, and consider the simpler model

$$S_{fit} = M_i + J_t + v_{fit} \tag{11-7}$$

To grasp its essence, imagine that there are no random disturbances ($v = 0$) and that there is only one firm, which sells three products

---

[1] Provided both exist in all time periods, regions, and industries included in the sample.

(tires, watches, clothes) over 5 years. Observations can be put in a 3-by-5 table or matrix whose rows correspond to the commodities and columns to the years:

$$\mathbf{S} = \begin{bmatrix} S_{11} & S_{12} & S_{13} & S_{14} & S_{15} \\ S_{21} & S_{22} & S_{23} & S_{24} & S_{25} \\ S_{31} & S_{32} & S_{33} & S_{34} & S_{35} \end{bmatrix}$$

Factor analysis seeks to express this table as the sum of two tables $\mathbf{M}$ and $\mathbf{J}$ of similar dimensions, the first with constant rows and the second with constant columns:

$$\mathbf{M} = \begin{bmatrix} M_1 & M_1 & M_1 & M_1 & M_1 \\ M_2 & M_2 & M_2 & M_2 & M_2 \\ M_3 & M_3 & M_3 & M_3 & M_3 \end{bmatrix} \qquad \mathbf{J} = \begin{bmatrix} J_1 & J_2 & J_3 & J_4 & J_5 \\ J_1 & J_2 & J_3 & J_4 & J_5 \\ J_1 & J_2 & J_3 & J_4 & J_5 \end{bmatrix}$$

In a practical problem this cannot be done exactly, particularly if several firms are involved. This is the familiar problem of conflicting observations, which is treated in Sec. 7.2. In practice, some compromise is found which gives the $\mathbf{M}$ and $\mathbf{J}$ that "fit best" the observations $\mathbf{S}$.

A graphic way to express the problem of factor analysis is the following. You are given a rectangular piece, say, 3 by 5 miles, of a topographical map with contour lines showing the elevation at various spots. You are supposed to find a landscape profile running from north to south and another one running from east to west with the property that, if you slide the bottom of the first perpendicularly along the humps and bumps of the second, the top crests describe the original surface of the 3-by-5 map. The same happens if you interchange the roles of the two profiles. The two profiles are kept always perpendicular to each other; and this is why the literature calls the two factors $\mathbf{M}$ and $\mathbf{J}$ *orthogonal* (that is to say, *right-angled*). (See Fig. 23.)

Computing differences among the various entries in $\mathbf{M}$ and $\mathbf{J}$ is a simple matter under the usual assumptions. Again, we minimize the expression

$$\sum_{fit} v_{fit}^2$$

with respect to $M_1, M_2, M_3, J_1, J_2, J_3, J_4, J_5$. Thus the solution for

M_1 is

$$\hat{M}_1 = \frac{\left\{\sum_{ft} S_{f1t} - F \sum_t J_t\right\}}{FT} \tag{11-8}$$

and that of J_3 is

$$\hat{J}_3 = \frac{\left\{\sum_{fi} S_{fi3} - F \sum_i M_i\right\}}{FI} \tag{11-9}$$

where F, I, T are the total number of firms, industries, and time periods, respectively. Note that, to estimate the degree of monopoly in the first industry, we need knowledge of inflation in all years; to estimate inflation in year 3, we need measures of monopoly for all

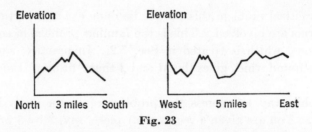

Fig. 23

industries. Equation (11-8) can be rationalized as follows: to estimate the effect of monopoly in the first industry, disregard the price-cost spread in all other industries, and compute the over-all (firm-to-firm and period-to-period) average spread in industry 1:

$$\frac{\sum_{ft} S_{f1t}}{FT}$$

From this deduct the average inflationary impact

$$\frac{\sum_t J_t}{T}$$

What is left is the monopoly impact.

11.5. Testing orthogonality

It is entirely possible for inflation's impact on the price-cost spread to be related to monopoly. Indeed, there is evidence from the Second World War that price control was more successful in monopolistic industries (and firms) than in competitive ones. A monopolist or monopolistic competitor is recognized and remembered by the public. If he takes advantage of inflation, he may lose goodwill or perhaps be sued by the government as an example to others. If monopoly and inflation interact in this way or in some other way, the linear model (11-7) is not applicable. Because it is simple, however, we may adopt it as our null hypothesis, fit it, and look for a systematic pattern discrepancy as a test of the hypothesis.

The formulas for doing this are rather complicated expressions, which I shall not bother to state. Intuitively the test is quite simple. If by rearranging *whole* rows and *whole* columns, table **S** can be made to have its highest entry in the upper left-hand corner, its smallest entry in the lower right-hand corner, with each row and column stepping down by equal amounts, the null hypothesis holds. For example,

$$\mathbf{S} = \begin{bmatrix} 12 & 15 & 11 \\ 14 & 17 & 13 \end{bmatrix}$$

can be rearranged thus:

$$\mathbf{S}' = \begin{bmatrix} 17 & 14 & 13 \\ 15 & 12 & 11 \end{bmatrix}$$

Note that

$$\mathbf{S}' = \begin{bmatrix} 15 & 12 & 11 \\ 15 & 12 & 11 \end{bmatrix} + \begin{bmatrix} 2 & 2 & 2 \\ 0 & 0 & 0 \end{bmatrix} \tag{11-10}$$

To state the same test in terms of our geographic profiles of Sec. 11.4: Cut up the original map into north-south strips, rearrange, and then glue them together. Then cut the resulting map into east-west strips and rearrange these. Should this procedure produce a map of a territory (1) sloping from its northwest corner down to its southeast corner, (2) with neither local hills nor saddle points, and (3) such that, if you stand anywhere on a given geographical parallel and take one step south, you step down by an equal amount, say, 3 feet, and (4) such that, likewise, if you start from any point on a fixed meridian, one eastward step loses the same elevation, say, 2.1 feet, then the factors are orthogonal.

In arithmetical terms, having estimated $M_1, M_2, \ldots, J_5$, rearrange the rows and columns so that the most monopolistic industry occupies the top row and the most inflationary year occupies the leftmost column. Compute the residuals

$$\hat{r}_{fit} = S_{fit} - \hat{M}_i - \hat{J}_t$$

and place their sums

$$\sum_f r_{it}$$

in the appropriate row and column. Any *run*, or large local concentration, of mostly positive or mostly negative residuals is evidence that monopoly and inflation have interaction effects (are not orthogonal factors).

11.6. Factor analysis and variance analysis

Unspecified factor analysis, the technique explained in this chapter, should be carefully distinguished from variance analysis (and from factor analysis in the principal components sense of the term). Both techniques make use of a row-column classification, and both usually proceed on the null hypothesis that rows and columns do not interact. But here the similarities end. Factor analysis *measures* the row and column effects for each row and column, i.e., it computes the unspecified variable. Variance analysis *attributes* various percentages of total variance[1] to differences among all rows, to differences among all columns, and the remainder to chance. Factor analysis ends with $I + T$ *estimates* $\hat{M}_1, \hat{M}_2, \ldots, \hat{M}_I; \hat{J}_1, \hat{J}_2, \ldots, \hat{J}_T$. Variance analysis ends with three *percentages* expressing row variance, column variance, and unexplained variance in terms of total variance.

[1] Total variance in terms of the example, model (11-7), is

$$\frac{\sum_{fit} (S_{fit} - \text{av } S)^2}{FIT}$$

where av S is av$[fit]S_{fit}$, or the average spread over the entire sample.

In the course of analysis of variance, row means ($14\frac{2}{3}$ and $12\frac{2}{3}$) and column means (16, 13, and 12) are computed, but they are only auxiliary quantities, not estimates of factor impacts. However, the *differences* in these two sets of means are equal respectively to the *differences* in the impact [(2 and 0) and (15, 12, and 11)] of the two variables into which $\mathbf{S}'$ is factorable [see equation (11-10)].

It is not my intention to go into the details of variance analysis. Just three comments about it:

1. The reason why people analyze variance and not the fourth or seventeenth moment of the sample is this: A normal distribution with zero mean (such as the error term v_{fit}) can be completely described by its variance. The variance is a *sufficient* estimate, for it contains all the information that is implicit in the assumed distribution.

2. Under orthogonality, row, column, and unexplained variances add up to total variance, just as the square on the hypotenuse equals the sum of the squares on the other sides of a right-angled (orthogonal) triangle.

3. Under normality and orthogonality, variance *ratios* have certain convenient distributions, which are suitable for testing the null hypothesis (that rows or columns differ only by chance).

Further readings

Harold W. Watts, "Long-run Income Expectations and Consumer Saving," in *Studies in Household Economic Behavior*, by Dernburg, Rosett, and Watts (Yale Studies in Economics, vol. 9, pp. 103–144, New Haven, Conn., 1958), makes judicious use of dummy variables.

Robert M. Solow, "Technical Change and the Aggregate Production Functions" (*Review of Economics and Statistics*, vol. 39, no. 3, pp. 312–320, August, 1957), computes the unspecified variable "technology" not, as we have done in Sec. 11.2, by interregional aggregation, but by using the marginal productivity theory of distribution.

Variance analysis is a vast subject. See KENDALL, vol. 2, chaps. 23 and 24.

CHAPTER 12

Time series

12.1. Introduction

A time series $\mathbf{x}(t) = [x(1), \ldots , x(T)]$ is a collection of readings, belonging to *different* time periods, of some price, quantity, or other economic variable. We shall confine ourselves to discrete, consecutive, and equidistant time points.

Like all the kinds of manifestations with which econometrics deals, economic time series, both singly and in combination, are generated by the systematic and stochastic logic of the economy. The same techniques of estimation, hypothesis searching, hypothesis testing, and forecasting that work elsewhere in econometrics work also in time series.

Why then a chapter on time series? Why indeed, were it not for the large amount of muddle and confusion we have inherited from many decades of well-intentioned but faulty investigations.

The earliest and most abused time series are charts of the business cycle and security market behavior. Desiring knowledge, business cycle "physiologists" avoided all models, assumptions, and hypotheses in the hope that the facts would speak for themselves. Pursuing profit, stock market forecasters have sought and are seeking (and their clients are buying) short cuts to strategic extrapolations; they have cared nothing about the logic, whether of the economy or of their methods. Their Economistry is the crassest of alchemies.

The key ideas of this chapter are these: Facts never speak for themselves. Every method of looking at them, every technique for analyzing them is an implicit econometric theory. To bring out the implicit assumptions for a critical look, we shall study averages, trends, indices, and other very common methods of manipulating data.

I do not mean to condemn the traditional approaches altogether. Certainly, physiology and "mere" description can do no harm—for ultimately they are the sources of hypotheses. To look for quick, cheap, and simple short cuts to forecasting is a reasonable research endeavor. Furthermore, modern machines can help by doing much of the dull work, provided that an intelligent being is available to study their output.

12.2. The time interval

Up to now I have carefully avoided any discussion of time. In the model of Chap. 1

$$C_t = \alpha + \gamma Z_t + u_t \tag{12-1}$$

what does $t = 1, 2, \ldots, T$ represent, and why not select different intervals?

The secret is that the time interval t, the parameters α and γ, the variables C and Z, and the stochastic term u must be defined not without thought of but with regard to one another. If the time interval is short, then γ must be the short-run marginal propensity to consume. If t is a year, then it makes sense for Z to be treated as predetermined. As the time interval is shortened, more and more variables change from predetermined to simultaneously determined. With shorter and shorter time periods, the causes that generate the random terms overlap more and more and invalidate the assumption of serially independent random disturbances.

In certain cases we deliberately reduce the number of time intervals of our data in order to bring time into agreement with the parameters and stochastic assumptions. For example, if we are trying to estimate a production or cost function and have hourly data for inputs and outputs, we may lump these into whole working days; otherwise the disturbances during the morning warm-up period, coffee break, lunch time, and the various peak fatigue intervals are not drawn from the same Urn of Nature.

The smoothing of time series must be done with care.   In the above example, if the purpose is to make the random disturbance come from the same Urn in each interval, then overlapping as well as nonoverlapping workdays will do.   If we also want the disturbances to be serially independent, then only nonoverlapping days should be used.

Digression on moving averages and sums

Moving averages differ from moving sums only by a constant factor P equal to the number of original intervals smoothed together.

If P is even $(= 2N)$ the average or sum should be centered on the boundary between intervals N and $N + 1$.   If $2N + 1$ intervals are averaged, center on the $(N + 1)$st.

There are many smoothing methods besides the unweighted moving average.   We are free to decide on the *span P* of the moving average and on the *weight* to be given each position within the span.   Given P successive points, we may wish to fit to them a least squares quadratic, logistic, or other curve.   Every particular curve implies a particular set of weights, and conversely.   Fitting a polynomial of degree Q through P points can be approximated by taking the simple moving average of a simple moving average of a simple moving average . . . enough times and with suitable spans.

All this is straightforward and rather dull, unaccompanied by theoretical justification.   What makes moving averages interesting is the claim that they can be used to determine and remove the trend of a time series.   We shall see in Sec. 12.8 how dangerous a technique this is.   As we shall see in Sec. 12.5, moving averages give rise to broad oscillations where none exist in the original series.

12.3. Treatment of serial correlation

The term *serial correlation*, or *autocorrelation*, means the nonindependence of the values u_t and $u_{t-\theta}$ of the random terms.   The term *autoregression* applies to values x_t and $x_{t-\theta}$ when cov $(x_t, x_{t-\theta}) \neq 0$.

In this section we consider briefly (1) the sources of serial correlation, (2) its detection, (3) the allowances and modifications, if any, that it occasions in our estimating techniques, (4) the consequences of not making these allowances and modifications.

Random terms are serially correlated when the time interval t is too short, when overlapping observations are used, and when the data from which we estimate were constructed by interpolation. Thus, if, in

$$C_t = \alpha + \gamma Z_t + u_t$$

t measures months or weeks, then the random term has to absorb the effects of the months' being different in length, weather, and holidays, effects which are not random in the short period but which follow a cycle of 365 days. If, however, t is measured in years, then all these influences are equalized, one year with another, and u_t loses some of its autocorrelation. Similarly, if successive sample points are dated "January to December," "February to January," "March to February," and so on, successive random terms are correlated at least 10/12 (10 being the number of months common to successive samples).

Frequently the raw materials of econometric estimation are constructed partly by interpolation. For instance, there is a census in 1950 and in 1960. Annual sample surveys in 1951, 1952, . . . measure births, deaths, and migrations; these data, cumulated from 1950, should square with the census population figure of 1960. Since this seldom happens, the discrepancy in the final published figures is apportioned (in general, equally) among the several years of the decade. The resulting annual figures for birth rate, etc., share equal portions of a certain error of measurement and are, therefore, correlated more than they otherwise would be. In a model that uses annual data on the birth rate and assumes that it is measured without error, it is the random term that absorbs the year-to-year correlation.

We shall illustrate with the simple model (12-1). There are two ways to detect serial correlation. One is to maintain the null hypothesis that none exists:

$$\text{cov } (u_t, u_{t-\theta}) = 0 \qquad (12\text{-}2)$$

estimate the model on this assumption, and then check whether $m_{(u_t)(u_{t-\theta})}$ is near zero. The other way is to maintain that the random disturbances do have a serial connection, such as

$$u_t = \zeta_1 u_{t-1} + \cdots + \zeta_\theta u_{t-\theta} + v_t \tag{12-3}$$

(with v_t random and nonautocorrelated), and estimate the ζs to see whether they are significantly different from zero.

The first method is arithmetically easier, though a less *powerful* test. This requires explanation. The likelihood function of our sample is the same as (2-4):

$$L = (2\pi)^{-S/2} \det (\mathfrak{o_{uu}})^{-\frac{1}{2}} \exp\left[-\tfrac{1}{2}\mathbf{u}(\mathfrak{o_{uu}})^{-1}\mathbf{u}\right]$$

where $\mathbf{u}$ stands for the successive random disturbances $(u_1, u_2, \ldots, u_S)$. In minimizing L by α and γ, we should get the greatest efficiency in $\hat{\alpha}$ and $\hat{\gamma}$ if we took account of the fact that $\mathfrak{o}$ is no longer diagonal when there is serial correlation among the disturbances. The null hypothesis cov $(u_t, u_{t-\theta}) = 0$, though it does not bias $\hat{\alpha}$ or $\hat{\gamma}$ or make them inconsistent, does nevertheless increase their sampling variances and covariances. The $\hat{u}$'s are computed with the help of the inefficient $\hat{\alpha}$ and $\hat{\gamma}$ and are themselves inefficient estimates of the true disturbances. Therefore $m_{(\hat{u}_s)(\hat{u}_{s-\theta})}$ is an inefficient (i.e., overspread) estimator of cov $(u_t, u_{t-\theta})$ and provides a flabby test of serial correlation. It does not reject the null hypothesis with so much confidence as a more powerful test (i.e., one associated with a very pinched distribution $m_{(\hat{u}_s)(\hat{u}_{s-\theta})}$).

Instead of testing by $m_{(\hat{u}_s)(\hat{u}_{s-\theta})}$ it is recommended that we compute the expression

$$D(\theta) = \frac{S}{S - \theta} \frac{\Sigma(\hat{u}_s - \hat{u}_{s-\theta})^2}{\Sigma(\hat{u}_s)^2}$$

which happens to have convenient properties, which are of no concern to the present discussion. It is easily seen that, if $m_{(\hat{u}_s)(\hat{u}_{s-\theta})} = 0$, then $D(\theta) = 2$. Large departures from this value indicate that the null hypothesis is untrue.

The second method for taking into account the serial correlation of the random disturbance is more efficient than the first, but biased. To see this, consider the special case

$$C_t = \alpha + \gamma Z_t + u_t \tag{12-4}$$
$$u_t = \zeta u_{t-1} + v_t \tag{12-5}$$

As good simultaneous-approach proponents, we combine the two equations as follows:

$$C_t - \zeta C_{t-1} = \alpha + \gamma(Z_t - \zeta Z_{t-1}) + v_t \qquad (12\text{-}6)$$

and maximize the joint likelihood of the random disturbances v with respect to the *three* parameters α, γ, ζ. Unfortunately, not only does this lead to a high-order system of equations, but the maximum likelihood estimates are biased. The reason for bias is the same as in Chap. 3, namely, that (12-6) is a model of decay.

There is yet a third method, which is somewhat biased and somewhat inefficient. First fit (12-4) by least squares, ignoring (12-5): this step is inefficient. Then compute ζ from (12-5) using the residuals $\hat{u}$ of the previous step: this introduces the bias. Next construct the new variables $c_t = C_t - \tilde{\zeta}C_{t-1}$, $z_t = Z_t - \tilde{\zeta}Z_{t-1}$ and fit by least squares $c_t = \alpha + \gamma z_t + w_t$ to get a new approximation to α and γ. Repeat the cycle any number of times.

When several equations have autocorrelated error terms, the biased second method always works in principle. The first and third methods are dangerous to use because we know practically nothing about how good $Sm_{\hat{u}_t \hat{u}_{t-\theta}}/(S - \theta)m_{\hat{u}\hat{u}}$ is as an estimator of the regression coefficient of u_t on $u_{t-\theta}$; nor do we know whether the cyclical procedure of the third method converges.

Matters get rapidly worse the more complicated the dependence of u_t on its past values.

12.4. Linear systems

Most business cycle analysis proceeds on the assumption (sometimes explicitly stated, more often not) that an economic time series $\mathbf{x}(t)$ is made up of two or more *additive* components $\mathbf{f}(t)$, $\mathbf{g}(t)$, . . . called the "trend," the "cycle," the "seasonal," and the "irregular." Trend, cycle, and seasonal are supposed to be, in some relevant sense, rather stable functions of time; the irregular is not. We shall use the expressions "irregular," "random component," "error," and "disturbance" interchangeably. The word "additive" signifies, as usual, lack of interaction effects among the components.[1]

In analyzing time series, the problem is to allocate the observed

[1] See Sec. 1.11.

fluctuations in x to its unknown additive components:

$$x(t) = f(t) + g(t) + h(t) + u_t \qquad (12\text{-}7)$$

and to find the shapes of f, g, and h: whether they are straight lines, polynomial or trigonometric functions, or other complicated forms.

As stated, the problem is indeterminate. The facts will never tell us either how many additive terms the expression in (12-7) should have or what shapes are best. As usual, we must maintain a hypothesis—that the trend is, say, a straight line:

$$f = \alpha + \beta t$$

that the cycle is some trigonometric function, e.g.,

$$\gamma \sin \left(\delta + \epsilon t \right)$$

and so forth, the problem being to estimate the Greek letters from data or to see how well a given formulation fits in comparison with some rival hypothesis.

Trigonometric functions can be approximated by lagged expressions, such as

$$g(t) = \gamma_0 + \gamma_1 x(t-1) + \gamma_2 x(t-2) + \cdots + \gamma_Q x(t-Q) + v_t \quad (12\text{-}8)$$

with appropriate coefficients. The term "linear" expresses the additivity of the components of (12-7) or the linear approximation of (12-8) or both. In this section and in several more, we shall consider linear systems of a single variable $x(t)$. Linearity in the second sense (above) is very handy, because in linear systems the number of lags in (12-8) and the values of the γs determine whether $g(t)$ oscillates, explodes, or damps; the initial value $g(0)$ determines only the amplitude of the fluctuations. In nonlinear systems amplitude and type are not separable in this way.

We shall devote Secs. 12.5 to 12.7 to *a priori* trendless systems; then, in Sec. 12.8, we shall inquire how we know a system to be trendless and, if it has a trend, how this trend can be removed.

12.5. Fluctuations in trendless time series

A trendless or a detrended time series can be *random, oscillating,* or *cyclical.* It is *random* if it can be generated by independent drawings from a definable Urn of Nature.   It is *cyclical* (or *periodic*) if it repeats itself perfectly every Ω time periods; it is *oscillatory* if it is neither random nor periodic.

A simple trigonometric function like $\sin (2\pi t/\Omega)$ or $\sin (2\pi t/\Omega) + b$ $\sin (2\pi t/\Omega)$ is strictly cyclical.   The combination of two or more trigonometric functions with incommensurate[1] periods Ω_1, Ω_2, . . . [for instance, $x(t) = \sin (2\pi t/\Omega_1) + \cos (2\pi t/\Omega_2)$] is not periodic but oscillatory.   Commensurate periods Ω_1, Ω_2, . . . appear in (12-7) only in the trigonometric terms sin, cos, tan, etc., and not as multiplicative factors, exponents, etc.

With the exception of purely seasonal phenomena (which are periodic), economic time series are overwhelmingly of oscillating type. Oscillations arise from three sources: (1) the summation of non-stochastic time series with incommensurate periods, (2) moving averages of random series, and (3) autoregressive systems having a stochastic component.

We can briefly dispose of the last case first.   If $x(t)$ is an autogressive variable

$$x(t) = \alpha_1 x(t - 1) + \cdot\ \cdot\ \cdot + \alpha_H x(t - H) + u_t \qquad (12\text{-}9)$$

whose systematic part would damp if u were to be continually **zero**, then $x(t)$ can be expressed as a weighted moving average of the random disturbances, and so the third case reduces to the second case above.[2]

The moving average of a random series, however, oscillates!   This proposition, the Slutsky proposition, shocks the intuition at first and, therefore, deserves some discussion.   Let us take a time series so long that we do not have to worry about any shortage of material to be averaged by moving averages.   Consider now a moving average spanning P of the original periods.   To facilitate the exposition, let us take P amply large.   Now the original series $u(t)$, if it is random, should itself be neither constant nor periodic.   Because if it is constant, it is not random.   And if it is periodic, a given value of u depends on the previous one; hence $u(t)$ is not random.   A truly random series is neither full of runs and patterns nor entirely bereft of them.   Just as a true die, once in a while, produces runs of sixes or aces, so a random

[1] Two real numbers are incommensurate when their ratio is not a rational number.

[2] See KENDALL, vol. 2, pp. 406–407.

time series occasionally exhibits a run. For the sake of illustration, suppose the run is 3 periods long and $u_{101} = u_{102} = u_{103} = 10$. Now consider what happens to its moving average in the neighborhood of the run. Let the span be large relative to the run, say, $P = 17$. Then the moving average has a run (less pronounced and more tapered) 19 periods long—that is to say, from the time that the right-hand end of the span includes u_{101} to the time that its left-hand end includes u_{103}. A moving average of a moving average of a random series oscillates even more.

These simple properties are vital for the statistical analysis of business cycles.

In the first place, the economic system itself operates somewhat like a moving average of random shocks: consumers, businesses, governments get buffeted around by random external and internal impulses, such as weather, a rush of orders, a rash of tax arrears; the economy takes most of these things in its stride; it does not adjust instantaneously and completely to the shocks, but rather cushions and absorbs them over considerably larger spans than their original duration. The Slutsky proposition accounts for business oscillations as the result of averaging random shocks.

In the second place, even if the economic system itself does no averaging, statisticians do. The national income, price indexes, and other data in all the fact books are averages or cumulants of one sort or another, frequently over time. Such data would exhibit oscillations even if the economy itself did not.

Finally, analysts who use the moving average technique (on otherwise flawless data from an economy that is innocent of averaging) either for detrending or for any other purpose may themselves introduce oscillations into their charts and so generate a business cycle where none exists.

12.6. Correlograms and kindred charts

According to the Slutsky proposition, if we want to analyze a time series we shall be well advised to leave it unsmoothed and try some direct attack.

It is natural to ask first whether a given trendless time series $x(t)$ is oscillating or periodic. In the nonstochastic case the question can be quickly settled by the unaided eye, detecting faithful repetition of a pattern, however complicated. In the stochastic cases the faithful repetition is obscured by the superimposed random effects and their echoes, if any.

Define *serial correlation of order θ* as the quantity

$$\rho(\theta) = \frac{\text{cov } (x_t, x_{t-\theta})}{(\text{var } x_t \text{ var } x_{t-\theta})^{\frac{1}{2}}}$$

A *correlogram* is a chart with θ on the horizontal axis and $\rho(\theta)$ or its estimate $r(\theta)$ on the vertical. A strictly periodic time series has a periodic correlogram with always the same silhouette and the same periodicity. If the former is damped, so is the latter. A moving average of random terms has a damped (or damped oscillating) correlogram of no fixed periodicity. A nonexplosive stochastic auto-regressive system like (12-9) is a damped wave of constant periodicity.

Correlograms are not foolproof. They may or may not identify correctly the type of model to which a given time series belongs. For instance, if the random term in (12-9) is relatively large, the correlogram of $x(t)$ will compromise between the strictly periodic silhouette of the exact autoregressive system $\alpha_1 x(t - 1) + \cdots + \alpha_H x(t - H)$ and the nonperiodic silhouette of the cumulated random terms $u_H + \alpha u_{H-1} + \cdots + \alpha^{H-1} u_1$. In general, it will neither damp progressively nor exhibit any fixed periodicity. This is very unfortunate, because, from *a priori* theory, we expect to meet such time series often in economics.

Business cycle and stock market analysts are often interested in turning points in a series and in forces bringing about these turning points rather than in the amplitude of the fluctuations. This leads naturally to *periodograms*. To take an example from astronomy, imagine that the time series $x(t)$ measures the angle of Mars and Jupiter with an observer on earth. We know this series to be analyzable into four components: the revolutions of Earth, Mars, and Jupiter round the sun plus the minor factor of the earth's daily rotation. Periodograms are supposed to show, from evidence in the time series itself, the four relevant periods $\Omega_1 = 365.26$ days, $\Omega_2 = 687$ days, $\Omega_3 = 11.86$ years, and $\Omega_4 = 24$ hours. This is a relatively easy matter if the series is nonstochastic, if we know beforehand that only four basic periods are involved, or both. The composite series fluctuates and undergoes accelerations, decelerations, and reversals occasioned by the movements of its four basic components. All this is captured by the formulas

$$A = \sum_s x(s) \cos \frac{2\pi s}{\Omega}$$

$$B = \sum_s x(s) \sin \frac{2\pi s}{\Omega}$$

where Ω is an unknown period. The periodogram is a chart with Ω on the horizontal and S^2 on the vertical axis. The value $S^2 = A^2 + B^2$ attains maxima when Ω takes on the values Ω_1, Ω_2, Ω_3, Ω_4. The technique works fairly well if $\mathbf{x}(t)$ is indeed composed of periodic (trigonometric) terms and a random component. It works very badly when $\mathbf{x}(t)$ is autoregressive, because the echoes of past random disturbances are of the same order of magnitude as the smaller periodic components of $x(t) = \alpha_1 x(t - 1) + \cdots + \alpha_H x(t - H)$ and claim the same attention as the latter in the formula for S^2. Like the correlogram, the periodogram fails us where it is most needed, that is, in the analysis of an economic time series which we know to be autoregressive and stochastic though we know nothing about the number and size of its Ωs.

12.7. Seasonal variation

The easiest periodic components to measure and allow for are those tied to astronomy. We know that the cycle of rain and shine repeats itself every 365 days, and we would naturally expect this to be reflected in any time series having to do with swim suits, umbrellas, or number of eggs laid by the average hen. The same is true of cycles imposed by custom or by the state, for instance, the seven-day recurrence of Sunday idleness, the Christmas rush, the preference of employees for July holidays. In all these cases the period itself is known, although it may be complicated by moving feasts, the varying number of days in a month, and the occasional occurrence of, say, a short month containing four Sundays plus Easter or a Friday the thirteenth. The problem here is not to find the seasonal *period* but its *profile*.

It is one thing to recognize and measure the seasonal profile and another to remove it. Sometimes we want to do the former, sometimes the latter, depending on our purpose.

If the purpose is to forecast cycles and trends, it is a false axiom that a seasonally adjusted series is a better series. The only time we are justified in taking out seasonal fluctuations is when we believe that businessmen know there is seasonality, expect it, and adjust to it in a routine way, either consciously in a microeconomic way or in their totality when many millions of their microeconomic decisions interact to form the business climate. So, for forecasting purposes, it is legitimate to wash out seasonal movements only when they are washed out of the calculations of consumers and businessmen. If a seasonal exists but people have not detected it, it should be left in. For instance, if it were true that the stock market had seasonal properties unknown to its traders, they should not be corrected for, because the participants mistake these for basic trends and react accordingly. Conversely if the relevant people think there is a seasonal when in fact none exists, its imagined effect should be allowed for by the forecaster of trends. Suppose, as an example, that the market believes that the U.S. dollar falls in the summer relative to the Canadian and rises in the winter. This imagined seasonal should be taken into account in analyzing the significance of monthly or quarterly import orders. To deseasonalize every time series may increase knowledge in all cases, but it increases forecasting accuracy only when the time has come when the market has learned all the real seasonals and imagines none where none exist.

Every formula either for measuring seasonals or for removing them is an implicit economic theory, which may be appropriate for one economic time series and inappropriate for another. For instance, treating the seasonal as an additive factor implies that a given absolute deviation from some normal or trend is equally important in all months. This is false in the case of, say, housing-construction starts in Labrador; the average number of these is, let us assume, 4 in December and 50 in July. Then 5 starts in December is a more serious departure than 51 in July. However, many analysts use additive seasonals for each and every time series.

If the genuine seasonal period is 12 months, its profile can be approximated by averaging the scores of several Januaries, then several Februaries, etc. This technique gives a biased estimate of the seasonal profile if the time series is autoregressive, unless random disturbances 12 months apart are independent. To see this, take (for simplicity only) the one-lag autoregressive model

$$x(t) = \alpha x(t - 1) + \gamma \sin \frac{2\pi t}{12} + u_t$$

and let 0 represent the first January and 12 the following one.   For simplicity, let us average the values $x(0)$ and $x(12)$ of just Januaries. Then we have

$$x(12) = \alpha^{12} x(0) + \alpha^{12} u_1 + \alpha^{11} u_2 + \cdots + \alpha u_{11} + u_{12} + \gamma \sin 2\pi$$

which involves a moving sum of random terms, and this sum oscillates, as we already know from Sec. 12.5.   The oscillation due to the random term will be confounded with the amplitude of the true seasonal. This will manifest itself in two ways: either the seasonal will seem to shift or, if it does not shift, it will contain the cyclical properties of the cumulated random effects.

12.8. Removing the trend

Ultimately, economic theory and not the facts tell us whether the trend (or longest-term movement) is linear or otherwise.   If we obtain the trend as what is left after cycles and seasonals have been taken out, the trend inherits all the diseases and pitfalls of the seasonals.

In particular, if we use a moving average to obtain the trend, we are almost certain to get it wrong.   To see this, suppose that we have a trendless cyclical and stochastic phenomenon, say

$$x_t = \sin \frac{2\pi t}{\theta} + u_t$$

depicted in Fig. 24.   If the span P of the moving average is longer than the true period θ, then the moving average (dashes in Fig. 24) exaggerates the oscillations and imposes a long wavy trend where none existed.   Or again, if the system is autoregressive and trendless,

$$x(t) = \alpha_1 x(t - 1) + \cdots + \alpha_H x(t - H) + u_t$$

the moving average of the random term contributes its oscillations to the systematic ones and, by the same process as that shown in Fig. 24, imposes a long, wavy trend.   Naturally, distortions like these arise when $x(t)$ truly contains some systematic trend. Moving averages distort both the trend and the cycles.

The *variate difference* method eliminates trends on the ground that any trend can be approximated by a polynomial of some degree N and that such a polynomial can be brought down to zero after $N + 1$ differentiations. Therefore, let

$$x(t) = \gamma_0 + \gamma_1 t + \cdots + \gamma_N t^N + f(t) + u_t \qquad (12\text{-}10)$$

where $f(t)$ and u_t are the cyclical and random factors. The method

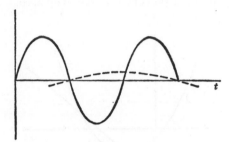

Fig. 24

proceeds as follows:

1. Difference (12-10) once:

$$x(t - 1) = \gamma_0 + \gamma_1(t - 1) + \cdots$$
$$+ \gamma_N t^{N-1} + f(t - 1) + u_{t-1} \quad (12\text{-}11)$$

2. Subtract (12-11) from (12-10) and call $y(t)$ the new variable $x(t) - x(t - 1)$. We do not need to write out $y(t)$ in full but note only that its trend is a polynomial of one degree less than the polynomial in (12-10) and that its random component is

$$v_t = u_t - u_{t-1} \qquad (12\text{-}12)$$

3. Do the same for $y(t)$, and define $z(t) = y(t) - y(t - 1)$; this too reduces the power of the trend and generates a random component

$$w_t = v_t - v_{t-1} = u_t - 2u_{t-1} + u_{t-2} \qquad (12\text{-}13)$$

4. Continue in this fashion as long as the estimated covariances m_{xx}, $m_{yy}/2$, $m_{zz}/6$ decrease. (The correcting denominators are discussed below.)

To see what is going on, consider the first quadrant of Fig. 25, where

$x(t)$ was taken to be a second-degree polynomial of t. Then $y(t)$ is a sloping straight line, and $z(t)$ is a level one. The variance of $x(t)$ is quite high, because x assumes many widely different values as t changes. The variance of $y(t)$ is smaller, because, though y varies, it varies more smoothly than x. And z does not vary at all. The variate difference method reduces the trend to z, and any remaining variation in the resulting series must be due to nontrend components.

Several things are wrong with this method. First, if x extends to the second quadrant of Fig. 25, say, symmetrically, its covariation with its lagged values may be very small or even zero. And, in general,

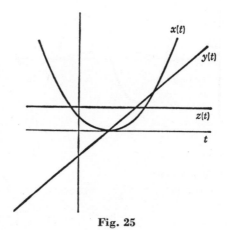

Fig. 25

a high-degree polynomial, because it twists and turns up and down, may exhibit a smaller lag covariance than a low-degree polynomial. Hence we should faithfully carry on successive differencing *in spite of* a drop in the series m_{xx}, m_{yy}, m_{zz}. But suppose we do. How are we to tell when the polynomial of unknown degree has finally died down? For meanwhile, as (12-12) and (12-13) show, we are performing moving averages of the cyclical component and, for all we know, this component may increase or decrease. Finally, the variate difference method cannot come to any stop if its cyclical component has a short lag. For instance, the first differences of 1, -1, 1, -1, . . . are 2, -2, 2, -2, . . . , and the first differences of the latter are 4, -4, 4, -4, and so on.

Now a word about the *correcting denominators*. If u_t itself is serially uncorrelated, then, from (12-12), the variance of v_t is twice that of u_t, since

$$\text{var } v_t = \text{cov } (u_t u_t) - 2 \text{ cov } (u_t, u_{t-1}) + \text{cov } (u_{t-1}, u_{t-1})$$
$$= \text{cov } (u_t, u_t) + \text{cov } (u_{t-1}, u_{t-1}) = 2 \text{ cov } (u_t u_t)$$

Similarly,

$$\text{var } w_t = \text{var } (u_t - 2u_{t-1} + u_{t-2})$$
$$= \text{var } u_t + 2 \text{ var } u_{t-1} + \text{var } u_{t-2} = 6 \text{ var } u_t$$

and so on for higher-order differences.

In my opinion, all these methods for detecting or eliminating the trend have serious imperfections. The way out is, as usual, to specify the algebraic form of the trend, the number of cyclical components acting on it, to make stochastic assumptions, and to maximize the likelihood of the sample. The procedure is very laborious; it is generally biased, but efficient. I think it represents the best we can ever do, and I am condemning the other methods only if they are pretentiously paraded as scientific. I do admit them as approximations to the ideal.

12.9. How not to analyze time series

The National Bureau of Economic Research has attracted a great deal of attention with its large-scale compilation and analysis of business cycle data. The compilation is done with such care, tenacity, and love as to earn the gratitude of all users of statistics. The analysis, however, has often been questioned. It proceeds roughly as follows:

1. Define a reference cycle for all economic activity. This is a conglomerate of the drift of several time series, accorded various degrees of importance.

2. Remove seasonal variations from the given series, say, carloadings or business failures.

3. Divide the given series into bands corresponding to the reference cycle.

4. Within each band express each January reading as a per cent of the average January in the band, and so on to December.

5. In each of the resulting specific cycles recognize nine typical

positions or phases.   The latter may be widely spaced, like an open accordion, in a long specific cycle or tightly in a short one.   The result is now considered to be *the* business cycle in carloadings, and constitutes the raw material for forecasting, for computing the irregular effects, and for checking whether the given series can be said to have its typical periodicity, amplitude, etc.   There are variations of the procedure, some *ad hoc*.   After what I said earlier in the chapter about the pitfalls of time series, I shall not make any further comment on the National Bureau's method.   Recently, electronic computations have been programmed, mainly for removing the seasonal.[1]   As they involve the use of several layers of moving averages, they are not altogether safe in the hands of an analyst ungrounded in mathematical statistics; since, however, the seasonal is the least likely to cause harm (after all, the period is correct), we may set this question aside.

12.10. Several variables and time series

In Secs. 12.1 to 12.9 we have considered variables that move in time subject to shocks and to laws of motion unconnected with any other variables.   It hardly needs stressing that endogenous economic variables are not of this kind, since all of them are generated jointly by the workings of the economic system.   One wonders of what use is the analysis of individual time series despite the heavy apparatus of correlograms, periodograms, and variate differences.

Assuming that several economic variables hang together structurally, what kinds of time series do they manifest?   Sections 12.11 and 12.12 discuss this problem.   If several economic variables are unconnected, how does a given combination of them behave?   The answer to this question (Sec. 12.13) provides a null hypothesis for judging the effectiveness of averages, sums, and a variety of business indicators, like the National Bureau of Economic Research "cyclical indicators" and "diffusion indexes" (Sec. 12.13).   The converse problems are also of great importance to the progress of business cycle research, because consideration of individual time series may enable us to infer the nature of the economic system without laboriously estimating each structural equation by the methods of Chaps. 1 to 9.

[1] See Julius Shiskin, *Electronic Computers and Business Indicators* (Occasional Paper 57, New York: National Bureau of Economic Research, 1957).

12.11. Time series generated by structural models

What kinds of time series are generated when the two variables x and y are structurally related? We shall take up this question first for nonstochastic relations and then for stochastic relations under various simplifying assumptions. All our models will be complete.

If the model is completely nonlagged, like the usual skeleton business cycle model

$$
\begin{aligned}
C &= \alpha + \beta Y \\
Y &= C + I
\end{aligned}
\tag{12-14}
$$

with investment taken as exogenous, then the time series for consumption and income have the same shape as the series for investment, as can be seen from the reduced form:

$$
\begin{aligned}
(1 - \beta)C &= \alpha + \beta I \\
(1 - \beta)Y &= \alpha + I
\end{aligned}
$$

In this example the agreement is not only in the timing of turns but in the phase as well, because investment, consumption, and income are positively related. In a more extended model

$$
\begin{aligned}
C &= \alpha + \beta Y \\
I &= \gamma + \delta G \\
Y &= C + I + G
\end{aligned}
\tag{12-15}
$$

where investment is endogenous, government expenditure is exogenous, and investment is discouraged by the latter ($\delta > 0$), all time series will coincide on timing; but when G grows I falls, and C and Y will fall if δ is less than -1 and will rise if it is greater.

If (12-14) and (12-15) are made stochastic, all endogenous variables absorb some of the random disturbances. The random disturbances apportion themselves, one year with another, according to a fixed pattern among the endogenous variables. For instance, if u is the random disturbance of the consumption function and v of the investment function, the reduced form of (12-15):

$$
\begin{aligned}
(1 - \beta)C &= (\alpha + \beta\gamma) + (\beta + \beta\delta)G + u + \quad \beta v \\
(1 - \beta)I &= (\gamma - \beta\gamma) + (\delta - \beta\delta)G + (1 - \beta)v \\
(1 - \beta)Y &= \quad (\alpha + \gamma) + (1 + \delta)G + u + \quad v
\end{aligned}
\tag{12-16}
$$

shows that the fluctuations and irregular components are in step, though they may differ in their amplitudes.

The variances of the three irregular components in (12-16) are proportional respectively to $\sigma_{uu} + 2\beta\sigma_{uv} + \beta^2\sigma_{vv}$, $(1 - \beta)\sigma_{vv}$, and $\sigma_{uu} + 2\sigma_{uv} + \sigma_{vv}$. Thus, if the two random terms are positively correlated ($\sigma_{uv} > 0$), income wobbles more than consumption and consumption more or less than investment, depending on the size of the marginal propensity to consume.

Let us now consider as a recursive model the market for fish. The men go to their boats with today's price in their minds, expecting it to prevail tomorrow, and work hard if the price is high. Thus tomorrow's supply depends on today's price plus weather (z). Should the price fall, the fishermen don't put the fish back into the sea; so at the end of the day all the fish is sold. Demand is ruled by current price only.

$$d = \alpha + \beta p + u$$
$$s = \gamma + \delta p_1 + \epsilon z + v \qquad (12\text{-}17)$$
$$s = d$$

The model can be solved for p as follows:

$$\alpha + \beta p_t + u_t = \gamma + \delta p_{t-1} + \epsilon z_t + v_t$$

which shows that price tends to zigzag (β negative, δ positive), falling with good weather and rising with bad, as we might expect. In (12-17), unlike case (12-16), the irregular components of the price and quantity time series are no longer constant multiples of each other, nor are they in step. This is so because randomly overeager demand ($u > 0$) affects not only today's price but, through its effect on the fishermen's efforts, contributes to a fall in tomorrow's price as well.

The connections among phase, amplitude, and irregularity in structurally related time series become very complicated as we increase the number of variables and as we admit more and more lags and cross lags. In any representative set of economic time series it would indeed be a marvel if closely similar patterns emerged, except between such series as sales of left and of right shoes. And yet the marvel seems to happen.

12.12. The over-all autoregression of the economy

Regardless of which came first, chickens and eggs in the long run have similar time series, because there can be no chicken without a previous combination of egg and chicken and there can be no egg without a previous chicken. Since the hatching capacity of a hen is fixed, say, 10 chicks per hen, and since the chicken-producing capacity of an egg is also fixed, say 1 to 1, the cycles in the egg population and in the hen population cannot possibly fail to exhibit a likeness—though, in particular short-run instances, random disturbances like Easter or a fox can grievously misshape now the one, now the other series. Orcutt has claimed[1] that something like this is true of the time series of the economy's endogenous variables. He states that the autoregressive relation

$$x_{t+1} = 1.3x_t - 0.3x_{t-1} + u_{t+1}$$

fairly describes the body of variables used by Tinbergen in his pioneering analysis of American business fluctuations.[2] Orcutt's result, if correct, would not exactly spell the end of structural estimation of econometric models, because the latter may be more efficient, less biased, etc. However, if a correct autoregression were discovered, it would certainly short-circuit a good deal of current research.

Orcutt's theorem holds only for systems whose exact part, by itself, is stable and nonexplosive. Orcutt also found that we can get better estimates of the over-all autoregression if we consider many time series simultaneously than if we consider them one at a time. This follows from the fact that Easter and foxes descend on eggs and hens independently, so that a grievous random dent in the egg population tends to be balanced by the relative regularity of the hen population.

In the absence of random shocks, all the interdependent variables have the same periodicity but different timing, amplitudes, and levels about which they fluctuate. With random shocks, the periodicities are destroyed more or less depending on the severity of the shocks and their incidence on particular variables. The unaided eye can seldom

---

[1] Reference is in Further Readings at the end of the chapter.

[2] Jan Tinbergen, *Statistical Testing of Business-Cycle Theories* (Geneva: League of Nations, 1939).

recognize the true periodicity. A highly sophisticated technique can screen out the autoregressive structure by combining observations from *all* time series, but it is so difficult to compute that one might as well specify a model in the ordinary way.

Exercises

12.A Let $g(t)$ and $k(t)$ be the population of gnus and of kiwis. Let β_i and δ_i be the age-specific birth and death rates for gnus and α_j and γ_j for kiwis. Disregard the question of the sexes. Let ϵ and ζ stand for input-output coefficients expressing the necessary number of kiwis a gnu must eat to survive, and conversely. Construct a model of this ecological system. Do something analogous for new cars and used cars.

12.B In a Catholic region, say, Quebec, the greater the number of priests and nuns, other things being equal, the smaller the birth rate, because the clergy is celibate. But the more numerous the clergy, other things being equal, the higher the birth rate of the laity, because of much successful preaching against birth control. Construct an ecological model for such a population.

12.C The more people, the more lice, because lice live on people. But the more lice, the more diseases and, hence, the fewer people. Construct the model, with suitable life spans for the average louse and human.

12.D According to the beliefs of a primitive tribe, lice are good for one's health, because they can be observed only on healthy people. (Actually the lice depart from the sick person because they cannot stand his fever.) Construct this model and compare with Exercise 12.C.

12.13. Leading indicators

An economic indicator is a sensitive messenger or representative of other economic phenomena. We search for indicators in the same spirit in which pathology examines the tongue and measures the pulse: for quickness, cheapness, and to avoid cutting up the patient to find out what is wrong with him.

A *timing indicator* is a time series that typically leads, lags, or coincides with the business cycle. Exactly what this means will occupy us later. We shall deal only with the leading indicators.

From what was said in Sec. 12.12, it comes as no surprise that certain economic time series, like Residential Building Contracts Awarded, New Orders for Durable Goods, and Average Weekly Hours in Manufacturing, should have a lead over Disposable Income, the Consumer Price Index, and so forth. The difficult questions are (1) how to insulate the cyclical components of each series from the trend, seasonal, and irregular; (2) how to tell whether leads in the sample period are genuine rather than the cumulation of random shocks; and (3) where phases are far apart, how to make sure that carloadings lead disposable income and not conversely, or that the Federal discount rate does lead and direct the money supply and not try belatedly to repair past mistakes. I am sure that, ultimately, one has to fall back on economic theory; one is forced to specify bits and pieces of any autoregressive econometric model, because no amount of mechanical screening of the time series themselves can answer the third question convincingly.

In 30 years of research the National Bureau of Economic Research has isolated about a dozen fairly satisfactory leading indicators out of 800-odd time series.[1] I think, however, that in nearly all cases, *a priori* considerations would have led to the selection of these leading series without the laborious wholesale analysis of hundreds and hundreds of time series. For instance, Average Hours Worked in Manufacturing is a good candidate for leading indicator of manufacturing activity because we know from independent observation that it is easier for a business establishment to take care of a moderate increase in orders by overtime than by hiring new workers and easier to tide over a lull by putting its workers on short time than by laying some off at the risk of losing them. All the sensible leading indicators thrown up in the National Bureau's screening are obvious in a similar way. An oddity like the production of animal tallow, which is said to lead better than many other series, could not have been discovered by *a priori* reasoning, but neither is it used by any sane forecaster, for a good empirical fit is no substitute for a sound reason.

Part of the findings of the National Bureau are, I think, tautological, because the timing indicators lead, lag, and coincide not with each other individually, but with the reference cycle, which is an index of

[1] See Geoffrey H. Moore, *Statistical Indicators of Cyclical Revivals and Recessions* (Occasional Paper 31, New York: National Bureau of Economic Research, 1950), particularly chap. 7 and appendix B.

"general business activity." The latter is a vague conglomerate of employment, production, price behavior, and monetary and stock market activity; therefore, it is no wonder at all that some series lead, some coincide with, and others lag behind it. The reference cycle is a useful summary, but we should not be misled into existential fallacies about it.

12.14. The diffusion index

A *diffusion index* is a number stating how many out of a given set of time series are expanding from month to month (or any other interval). Diffusion indexes can be constructed from any set of series whatsoever and according to a variety of formulas, of which I shall discuss just three.

There are two reasons why one might want to construct a diffusion index. One is the belief that a business cycle starts in some corner of the economic system and propagates itself on the surrounding territory like a forest fire. This says in effect that the diffusion index is a cheap short-cut autoregressive econometric model. The second reason is that the particular formula used to construct the index captures in a handy way the logic of economic behavior.

Three different formulas have been suggested for the diffusion index:

Formula A   Per cent of the series expanding
Formula B   Per cent of the series reaching turns
Formula C   Average number of months the series have been expanding

Research by exhaustion argues that we ought to try all these formulas on all time series and choose the formula that gives pragmatically the best results. This can be done quite cheaply on the Univac. I think such a procedure will frustrate our search for good indicators, because each formula embodies a different theory of economic behavior, not universally suitable.

Formula A is justified by the classical type of business cycle, where income, employment, prices, hours, inventories, production, and so on, and their components move up and down in rough agreement or with characteristic lags. Suppose, however, that the authorities control totals—employment, some price index, credit, or the balance of payments.   The result is "rolling readjustment" rather than cycles. Formula A has lost its relevance.   In a world of rolling readjustment this formula will show an uneventful record and will not be able to indicate, much less predict, sectional crises hiding under a calm total.

Formula B is justified if consumers and business are more sensitive to turns, however mild, than to accelerations, however violent.   Investment plans are likely to be of this kind.   As long as there is expansion in demand, any overexpansion will be made good eventually.   If there is contraction, however small, the mistake is more obvious, and panic may easily result.   On the other hand, there are many areas in both the consumer and the business sectors where small turns are not taken seriously.   Formula B, therefore, can be used to best advantage in studying certain investment series (like railways' orders of rolling stock) but is counterprescribed elsewhere.

Formula C gives great emphasis to reversals.   Take a component that has been slowly expanding for some months, then turns down briefly.   Formula C registers (for this component) 1, 2, 3, etc., up to a large positive number, then -1 (for the first month of contraction). The more sustained the expansion, the more violently does the formula register a halt or small reversal.   This formula, then, is appropriate where habit and momentum play an important part.   Where could we possibly want to apply it?

Hire-purchase may be related to disposable income in some way that agrees with the logic of formula C.   Suppose that small increases in income go into down payments and time payments for more and more gadgets; if so, a small fall in income would put a complete stop to new hire-purchase, because the family would continue its contractual time payments on the old gadgets and would not be likely to cut into food, clothing, and recreation to buy new gadgets.   This is a theory of consumer behavior, and formula C is a convenient way to express it short of an econometric equation.

Exercises

12.E   Construct diffusion indexes by each formula from the two time series below:

Series 1	100,	96,	90,	96,	97,	95,	97
Series 2	100,	99,	102,	100,	100,	101,	107

and compare the cyclical behavior of the indexes with that of the sum of the two series.

12.F   In Exercise 12.E, series 2, replace the 99 by 101, and construct formula A.   Must turning points in the sum be preceded by turning points in the index?

12.G   Construct an example to show that an index according to formula C can be completely insensitive to the sum of the component series.

12.H   Show by example the converse of Exercise 12.G, namely, that swings in the diffusion index formula C need not herald turns (or any change whatsoever) in the sum of the component series.

12.15. Abuse of long-term series

One unfortunate by-product of time series analysis is that it requires long time series with which to work, and several research organizations have responded enthusiastically to the challenge.

For example, I have heard urgings that we construct Canadian historical statistics for the purpose of sorting out timing indicators, on the ground that what took the National Bureau 30 years can now be done in 30 hours electronically.   I think this kind of work quite futile, for a few moments' reflection will convince us of its negative results. The Canadian economy, compared with the American, is small and relatively unbalanced; therefore, Canadian historical statistics will have a very large irregular component, which will overwhelm the fine structural relationships we want to uncover.   The Canadian economy, being open, responds to impulses from abroad; therefore, even if we had good domestic historical time series, our chances of finding among them good indicators are slim.   We also know that the Canadian economy is "administered" (it has more governments per capita than we have and more industrial concentration); so the developments that are foreshadowed by the indicators are likely to be anticipated by the big policy makers, with the result that predictions go foul.   We know that Canada is and will be growing fast and that the past (on which all indicators rely) will not be a dependable guide.

My guess is that the earliest useful year for time series on bread baking is somewhere around 1920.   For iron ore shipments it is 1947, the year when certain Great Lakes canals were deepened.   However,

for housing demand as a function of family formation, many decades
or even centuries might prove to contain valid information.

There are many good reasons why we might want to construct
uniformly long historical statistics, but certainly the needs of cycle
forecasting is not one of them.

12.16. Abuse of coverage

An unfortunate by-product of diffusion index analysis is that it
encourages the construction of complete sets of data when incomplete
ones would be more satisfactory.   This is so because the timing and
irregular features of the diffusion index change with the number of
series included in it.

Let us suppose that we want to forecast industrial production by
means of average weekly hours worked; the series rationalized in
Sec. 12.13 is a possible leading indicator.   If hours worked come broken
down by industry, we suspect we might do better if we use a diffusion
index of the basic series rather than the over-all average.

Now our first impulse is to look at the published series for Hours
Worked and make sure that they give complete coverage by industry
and by locality and that the series have no gaps in time.   After all,
we want to forecast for all industry and for the entire country.   Yet it
is unreasonable to desire full coverage.

First, some industries employ labor as a fixed, not a variable, input.
A generating station, if it is operated at all, is tended by a switchman
24 hours a day, regardless of its output.   Labor is uncorrelated with
output.   Here is a case where coverage does harm to our forecast,
because it introduces two uncorrelated variables on each side of the
scatter diagram, so to speak.

Second, in the service industries, the physical measure of output *is*
labor input, because this is how the compilers of government statistics
measure the production of services.   If we insist on coverage of the
services, we get trivial correlations, not good forecasts.

Third, during retooling it is possible to have long working hours and
no industrial production.   What should we do?   Throw out entirely
any industry that has retooling periods?   Not at all.   It is enough to
suppress temporarily from consideration the data for this industry
until the experts tell us that retooling and catching up on backlog are

over.   A deliberate time gap in the statistics improves them.   This
method, though it appears to be wasting information, actually uses
more, for it includes the fact that there has been a retooling period.
The fact that the diffusion index is dehomogenized is a flaw of a second
order of importance.

In this way we select statistics of average hours worked to use in
forecasting industrial production which are a statistician's nightmare:
they have time gaps, they are unrepresentative, and they do not
reconcile with national accounts Labor Income when they are multiplied by an average of wage rates.

Similarly, for statistics that are most useful in forecasting, it is
not necessary that they be classifiable into grand schemes, such as
the National Income, Moneyflows, or Input-Output Tables.   The
Canadians plan to start compiling data on Lines of Credit agreed
upon by chartered banks and their customers but not yet credited to
the customer's account.   Such a series, I think, will prove a better
predictor than the present one, Business Loans.   Now, if we had
information on Lines of Credit, it would not fit any existing global
scheme and would not become any more useful if it did.   For forecasting purposes, I see no excuse for creating a matrix of Inter-sector
Contingent Liabilities or for constructing a Balance of Withdrawable
Promises account.

12.17. Disagreements between cross-section and time series estimates

It is very puzzling to find that careful studies of the consumption
function derived from time series give a significantly larger value for
the marginal propensity to consume than equally competent studies of
cross-section data.   Three kinds of explanations are available: (1)
algebraic and (2) statistical properties of the model explain the discrepancy; and (3) cross-section data and time series data measure
different kinds of behavior.   We shall concentrate on explanations
1 and 2 in order to show that algebra and statistics alone account for
much of the difference and that to this extent explanations of the third
category are redundant.

Cross-section data are figures of income, consumption, etc., by
individual families in a given fixed time period.   Time series are data

about a given family's consumption and income through time or about national consumption and income through time.

Algebraic differences

The shape of the consumption function can breed differences. If the family consumption function is nonlinear, say,

$$c = \alpha + \beta y + \gamma y^2 + u \tag{12-18}$$

then the consumption function connecting average income av y and average consumption av c or total income Y and total consumption C will look different from equation (12-18), even if all families have the same consumption function and if the distribution of income remains constant. To see this, take just two families,

$$c_1 = \alpha + \beta y_1 + \gamma (y_1)^2 + u_1$$
$$c_2 = \alpha + \beta y_2 + \gamma (y_2)^2 + u_2$$

add together and divide by 2 to get

$$\text{av } c = \alpha + \beta \text{ av } y + 2\gamma(\text{av } y)^2 - \gamma y_1 y_2 + \text{av } u \tag{12-19}$$

and, in general, with N individuals,

$$\text{av } c = \alpha + \beta \text{ av } y + N\gamma(\text{av } y)^2 - \gamma \sum_{i<j} y_i y_j + \text{av } u \tag{12-20}$$

One might argue that, when income distribution remains unchanged, the cross term $\Sigma y_i y_j$ remains constant and is absorbed into the estimate of α. But this is false, because the cross term appears in (12-20) multiplied by γ, another unknown parameter, whose estimate is bound up with the estimates of α and β in the least squares (or other) formulas. The discrepancy between (12-20) and (12-19) affects the estimates of all three parameters α, β, and γ if no allowance is made for the extra terms of the average consumption function. The last two terms of (12-20) are equal to

$$\gamma \sum_{i=1}^{N} \frac{y_i^2}{N}$$

that is to say, the raw moment m'_{vv} of the family incomes. It follows that, for time series and cross-section studies to give agreeing results, the average (or the total) consumption function must contain a term m'_{yy} expressing inequality of income, even if this inequality should remain unchanged from year to year. Moreover, neither the sample variance of av y nor the Pareto index is suitable for the correction in question.

If income distribution varies with time, to get the two approaches to agree our correction must be more elaborate, because the factor

$$\sum_{i<j} y_i y_j$$

must be calculated anew for each year of the data. If we have no complete census of all families, a sample estimate of $\Sigma y_i y_j$ will be better than nothing. If a census of families exists but we are in a hurry, again we can approximate $\Sigma y_i y_j$ to any desired degree by taking the families in large income strata.

Statistical differences

Let us assume that the consumption function of a family is linear and constant over time and that it involves another variable x, reflecting some circumstance of the family, like age.

$$c = \alpha + \beta y + \gamma x + u \tag{12-21}$$

However, let the characteristic x, as time passes, have a constant distribution among the several families. For example, in a stationary population, the ages of the totality of families remains unchanged, although the age of any given family always increases. If we aggregate (12-21) we get

$$\text{av } c = \alpha + \beta \text{ av } y + \gamma \text{ av } x + \text{av } u \tag{12-22}$$

but x, being a constant, is absorbed into the constant term when we estimate (12-22). Not so if we trace the history of one such family by estimating (12-21) from time series.

In practice there is a further complication: the characteristic x is not independent of the family's income; thus, $\hat{\beta}$ and $\hat{\gamma}$ are shaky estimates in (12-21) because of multicollinearity. This is an additional reason why time series and cross sections disagree.

Thus, we do not need to go so far afield as to postulate several kinds of consumption functions (long-term, short-term) to explain these discrepancies. If, after we have corrected for the algebraic and statistical sources of discrepancy, some further disagreement remains unexplained, that is the time for additional theories.

Further readings

KENDALL, vol. 2, devotes two lucid chapters to the algebra and statistics of univariate time series.

The proof that ignoring the serial correlation of the random term in a single equation leaves least squares estimates unbiased and consistent can be found in F. N. David and J. Neyman, "Extension of the Markoff Theorem on Least Squares" (*Statistical Research Memoirs*, vol. 2, pp. 105–116, December, 1938).

How to treat serial correlation is discussed by D. Cochrane and G. H. Orcutt, "Application of Least Square Regression to Relationships Containing Auto-correlated Error Terms" (*Journal of the American Statistical Association*, vol. 44, no. 245, pp. 32–61, March, 1949).

Eugen Slutsky, "The Summation of Random Causes as the Source of Cyclical Processes" (*Econometrica*, vol. 5, no. 2, pp. 105–146, April, 1957), is rightly famous for its contribution to theory and its interesting experimental examples with random series drawn from a Soviet government lottery.

Correlogram and periodogram shapes are discussed in KENDALL, vol. 2, chap. 30.

The brief discussion of autocorrelation, with examples, in BEACH, pp. 176–180, is simple and useful.

The early article by Edwin B. Wilson, "The Periodogram of American Business Activity" (*Quarterly Journal of Economics*, vol. 48, no. 3, pp. 375–417, May, 1934), is both ambitious and sophisticated.

Tjalling C. Koopmans, in his review, entitled "Measurement without Theory," of Arthur F. Burns and Wesley C. Mitchell's *Measuring Business Cycles* (*Review of Economic Statistics*, vol. 29, no. 3, pp. 161–172, August, 1947), delivers a classic and definitive criticism of some investigators' avoidance of explicit assumptions. All would-be chartists should read it. Koopmans also gives, on p. 163, a summary account of the National Bureau method for isolating cycles.

J. Wise, in "Regression Analysis of Relationships between Autocorrelated Time Series" (*Journal of the Royal Statistical Society*, ser. B, vol. 18, no. 2, pp. 240–256, 1956), shows that, in recursive systems of two or more equations, least squares is biased both when the random terms of the separate equations are interdependent and when the random term of either equation is serially correlated.

The reference of Sec. 12.12 is G. H. Orcutt, "A Study of the Autoregressive Nature of the Time Series Used for Tinbergen's Model of the Economic System of the United States 1919–1932," with discussion (*Journal of the Royal Statistical Society*, ser. B, vol. 10, no. 1, pp. 1–53, 1948). Arthur J. Gartaganis, "Autoregression in the United States Economy, 1870–1929"

(*Econometrica*, vol. 22, no. 2, pp. 228–243, April, 1954), uses much longer time series and concludes that the over-all autoregressive structure changed drastically around the year 1913.   Gartaganis uses six lags.

I have discussed the mathematical properties of the diffusion index in "Must the Diffusion Index Lead?" (*American Statistician*, vol. 11, no. 4, pp. 12–17, October, 1957).   Geoffrey Moore's comments are on pp. 16–17.

Trygve Haavelmo, "Family Expenditures and the Marginal Propensity to Consume" (*Econometrica*, vol. 15, no. 4, pp. 335–341, October, 1947), reprinted as Cowles Commission Paper 26, affords a good exercise in the decoding of compact econometric argument. Haavelmo deals with the discrepancies arising from different ways of measuring the consumption function.

Layout of computations

I recommend a standard layout, no matter how large or small the model or what estimating procedure one plans to use (least squares, maximum likelihood, limited information) or what simplifying assumptions one has made. There are three general rules to follow:

1. Scale to avoid large rounding errors and to detect other errors more easily. Scaling should be applied in two stages.
   a. Scale the variables.
   b. Scale the moments.
2. Use check sums.
3. Compute all the basic moments. This may seem redundant, but is actually very efficient if one wants
   a. To compute correlations.
   b. To experiment with alternative models.
   c. To get least squares first approximations.
   d. To select the best instrumental variables.

The rules in detail

Stage 1

Scale the variables. Express all of them in units of measurement (say, cents, tens of dollars, thousands, billions, etc.) that reduce all the variables to comparable magnitudes. Scale the units so as to bring the variables (or most of them) into the range from 0 to 1. For instance:

National income	$x_1 = 0.475$ trillion dollars
Hourly wage rate	$x_2 = 0.182$ tens of dollars
Population	$x_3 = 0.165$ billions
Price of platinum	$x_4 = 0.945$ hundreds of dollars per ounce

This, rather than the range 1 to 10 or 10 to 100, is preferred, because we shall include an auxiliary variable identically equal to 1. Then all variables, regular and auxiliary, are of the same order of magnitude.

Stage 2

Arrange the raw observations as in Table A.1. Note that the endogenous variables, the y's, are followed by their check sum Y and that, in addition to all the exogenous variables $z_1, z_2, \ldots, z_{H-1}$, we devote a column to the constant number 1, which is defined as the last exogenous variable z_H. These are then followed by the check sum Z of the exogenous variables including $z_H = 1$ and by a grand sum $X = Y + Z$.

Stage 3

The *raw moment* of variable p on variable q is defined as

$$m'_{pq} = \Sigma p_s q_s$$

where the sum is over the sample. A *raw moment* is not the same thing as the simple *moment* m_{pq} defined in the Digression of Sec. 1.2. The simple moment m_{pq} is also called *the (augmented) moment from the mean of variable p on variable q*.

Compute the raw moments of all variables on all variables. This gives the symmetrical matrix $\mathbf{m}'$ of moments, shown in Table A.2. In Table A.2 the symbol m' is omitted, and only the subscripts appear; for instance, $y_G y_2$ stands for $m'_{y_G y_2}$.

Table A.1
Arrangement of raw observations

Time	Endogenous variables	Check sum	Exogenous variables		Check sum	Grand sum
			Regular	Aux.		
1	$y_1(1)$ $\cdots$ $y_G(1)$	$Y(1)$	$z_1(1)$ $\cdots$ $z_{H-1}(1)$	1	$Z(1)$	$X(1)$
2	$y_1(2)$ $\cdots$ $y_G(2)$	$Y(2)$	$z_1(2)$ $\cdots$ $z_{H-1}(2)$	1	$Z(2)$	$X(2)$
3	$y_1(3)$ $\cdots$ $y_G(3)$	$Y(3)$	$z_1(3)$ $\cdots$ $z_{H-1}(3)$	1	$Z(3)$	$X(3)$
.	.	.	.	.	.	.
.	.	.	.	.	.	.
.	.	.	.	.	.	.
S	$y_1(S)$ $\cdots$ $y_G(S)$	$Y(S)$	$z_1(S)$ $\cdots$ $z_{H-1}(S)$	1	$Z(S)$	$X(S)$

Table A.2

y_1y_1 $\cdots$ y_1y_G	y_1Y	y_1z_1 y_1z_2 $\cdots$ y_1z_{H-1}	$y_1\cdot 1$	y_1Z	y_1X
. $\quad$.	.	.	.	.	.
. $\quad$.	.	.	.	.	.
. $\quad$.	.	.	.	.	.
y_Gy_1 $\cdots$ y_Gy_G	y_GY	y_Gz_1 y_Gz_2 $\cdots$ y_Gz_{H-1}	$y_G\cdot 1$	y_GZ	y_GX
Yy_1 $\cdots$ Yy_G	YY	Yz_1 Yz_2 $\cdots$ Yz_{H-1}	$Y\cdot 1$	YZ	YX
z_1y_1 $\cdots$ z_1y_G	z_1y	z_1z_1 z_1z_2 $\cdots$ z_1z_{H-1}	$z_1\cdot 1$	z_1Z	z_1X
z_2y_1 $\cdots$ z_2y_G	z_2Y	z_2z_1 z_2z_2 $\cdots$ z_2z_{H-1}	$z_2\cdot 1$	z_2Z	z_2X
.	.	.	.	.	.
.	.	.	.	.	.
.	.	.	.	.	.
$z_{H-1}y_1$ $\cdots$ $z_{H-1}y_G$	z_{H-1}	$z_{H-1}z_1$ $z_{H-1}z_2$ $\cdots$ $z_{H-1}z_{H-1}$	$z_{H-1}\cdot 1$	$z_{H-1}Z$	$z_{H-1}X$
$1\cdot y_1$ $\cdots$ $1\cdot y_G$	$1\cdot Y$	$1\cdot z_1$ $1\cdot z_2$ $\cdots$ $1\cdot z_{H-1}$	$1\cdot 1$	$1\cdot Z$	$1\cdot X$
Zy_1 $\cdots$ Zy_G	ZY	Zz_1 Zz_2 $\cdots$ Zz_{H-1}	$Z\cdot 1$	ZZ	ZX
Xy_1 $\cdots$ Xy_G	XY	Xz_1 Xz_2 $\cdots$ Xz_{H-1}	$X\cdot 1$	XZ	XX

Stage 4

Compute the augmented moments from the mean of each variable (except $z_H = 1$) on each variable, e.g.,

$$m_{x_1x_2} = Sm'_{x_1x_2} - m'_{x_1 \cdot 1}m'_{1 \cdot x_2}$$

This is done very easily because $m'_{x_1 \cdot 1}$ and $m'_{x_2 \cdot 1}$ are always on the level indicated by the arrows and in the row and column corresponding to $m'_{x_1x_1}$.

This procedure gives a square symmetric matrix **m** of moments from the mean. The new matrix contains one row and one column less than the matrix **m′**.

Stage 5

Rule for check sums. In both **m** and **m′** any entry containing a capital Y (or Z) is equal to the sum of all entries in its row that contain lower-case y's (or z's). Any entry containing a capital X is equal to the sum of everything that precedes it in the row.

All these things are true in the vertical direction, since the matrices **m′** and **m** are symmetric.

Stage 6

Scale the moments. This step is not always possible. Scan the *symmetric* matrix **m**. If it contains any row (hence, column) of entries all (or nearly all) of which are very large or very small relative to the rest of the rows and columns, divide or multiply *the entire offending row and column* by an appropriate power of 10. The purpose is to make the matrix **m** contain entries as nearly equal as possible. When moments have comparable magnitudes, matrix operations on them are very accurate, rounding errors are small, and calculating errors can be readily detected.

Keep accurate track of the variables that have been scaled up or down in stages 1 and 6 and of how many powers of 10 in each stage and altogether.

Stage 7

Coefficients of correlation. These can be computed very easily from **m**, but unfortunately the checks do not work in this case. So drop the check sums and consider only part of **m**. The sample correlation coefficient between, say, the variables y_g and z_h is

$$r^2(y_g, z_h) = \frac{(m_{y_g z_h})^2}{m_{y_g y_g} m_{z_h z_h}}$$

Coefficients of correlation are used informally to screen out the most promising models (see Chap. 10 on bunch maps).

Matrix inversion

This is a frequent operation in estimating medium and large systems. Details for computing

$$\mathbf{M}^{-1} \qquad \text{and} \qquad \mathbf{M}^{-1}\mathbf{N}$$

are given in KLEIN, pp. 151ff. There are various clever devices for inverting a matrix and performing the operation $\mathbf{M}^{-1}\mathbf{N}$. Electronic computers have standard programs, and it is well to use them if they are available. If **M** is small in size and if both $\mathbf{M}^{-1}$ and $\mathbf{M}^{-1}\mathbf{N}$ are wanted, do the following: Write side by side the matrix **M**, the unit matrix of the same size, and then **N**.

$$[\mathbf{M}][\mathbf{I}][\mathbf{N}]$$

Then perform linear combinations on the rows of the entire new matrix [**MIN**] in such a way as to reduce **M** to a unit matrix. When you have finished, you will have obtained

$$[\mathbf{I}][\mathbf{M}^{-1}][\mathbf{M}^{-1}\mathbf{N}]$$

For example, let

$$\mathbf{M} = \begin{bmatrix} 2 & 4 \\ 1 & 6 \end{bmatrix} \qquad \mathbf{N} = \begin{bmatrix} 6 & 30 & 50 \\ 2 & 1 & 3 \end{bmatrix}$$

We shall trace the evolution of [**M**][**I**][**N**] into [**I**][$\mathbf{M}^{-1}$][$\mathbf{M}^{-1}\mathbf{N}$].

$$(\mathbf{MIN})_0 = \begin{bmatrix} 2 & 4 & | & 1 & 0 & | & 6 & 30 & 50 \\ 1 & 6 & | & 0 & 1 & | & 2 & 1 & 3 \end{bmatrix}$$

Divide the first row by 2.

$$(\mathbf{MIN})_1 = \begin{bmatrix} 1 & 2 & | & \tfrac{1}{2} & 0 & | & 3 & 15 & 25 \\ 1 & 6 & | & 0 & 1 & | & 2 & 1 & 3 \end{bmatrix}$$

In this new matrix, subtract row 1 from row 2.

$$(\mathbf{MIN})_2 = \begin{bmatrix} 1 & 2 & \frac{1}{2} & 0 & 3 & 15 & 25 \\ 0 & 4 & -\frac{1}{2} & 1 & -1 & -14 & -22 \end{bmatrix}$$

Divide the new second row by 2.

$$(\mathbf{MIN})_3 = \begin{bmatrix} 1 & 2 & \frac{1}{2} & 0 & 3 & 15 & 25 \\ 0 & 2 & -\frac{1}{4} & \frac{1}{2} & -\frac{1}{2} & -7 & -11 \end{bmatrix}$$

Subtract the new second row from the first.

$$(\mathbf{MIN})_4 = \begin{bmatrix} 1 & 0 & \frac{3}{4} & -\frac{1}{2} & 3\frac{1}{2} & 22 & 36 \\ 0 & 2 & -\frac{1}{4} & \frac{1}{2} & -\frac{1}{2} & -7 & -11 \end{bmatrix}$$

Divide the new second row by 2.

$$(\mathbf{MIN})_5 = \begin{bmatrix} 1 & 0 & \frac{3}{4} & -\frac{1}{2} & 3\frac{1}{2} & 22 & 36 \\ 0 & 1 & -\frac{1}{8} & \frac{1}{4} & -\frac{1}{4} & -3\frac{1}{2} & -5\frac{1}{2} \end{bmatrix}$$

$$\underbrace{}_{[\mathbf{I}]} \quad \underbrace{}_{[\mathbf{M}^{-1}]} \qquad \underbrace{}_{[\mathbf{M}^{-1}\mathbf{N}]}$$

One can compute a string of "quotients" $\mathbf{M}^{-1}\mathbf{N}$, $\mathbf{M}^{-1}\mathbf{P}$, $\mathbf{M}^{-1}\mathbf{Q}$, etc., by tacking on $\mathbf{N}$, $\mathbf{P}$, $\mathbf{Q}$ and performing the linear manipulations. This technique works in principle for all sizes of matrices with more than three or four rows, but it consumes a lot of paper and time.

Stepwise least squares

Estimating the parameters of

$$y = \gamma_0 + \gamma_1 z_1 + \gamma_2 z_2 + \gamma_3 z_3 + \cdots + \gamma_H z_H + u$$

by desk calculator, according to Cramer's rule, or by matrix inversion is a formidable task when H is greater than 3. The stepwise procedure about to be explained may be slow, but it has three advantages over the other methods:

1. It can be stopped validly at any stage.

2. It possesses excellent control over rounding and computational errors.

3. We do not have to commit ourselves, ahead of time and once and for all, on how many decimal places to carry in the course of computations, but we may rather carry progressively more as the estimates are successively refined.

I shall illustrate the method by the simple case

$$w = \alpha x + \beta y + \gamma z + u$$

where (in violation of the usual conventions) w is endogenous, and x, y, z are exogenous. For the sake of illustration let us assume that, in the sample we happen to have drawn, the exogenous variables are "slightly" intercorrelated, so that m_{xy}, m_{xz}, m_{xu}, m_{yz}, m_{yu}, m_{zu} are small numbers, although, of course, $m_{xx} = m_{yy} = m_{zz} = 1$.

Step 1

On the basis of *a priori* information, arrange the exogenous variables from the most significant to the least significant, that is to say, according to the imagined size of the parameters α, β, γ, disregarding their signs:

$$|\alpha| \geq |\beta| \geq |\gamma|$$

Step 2

To estimate a first approximation to α, compute $\tilde{\alpha}_1 = m_{wx}/m_{xx}$ as an approximation to the true value. Let $\tilde{\alpha}_1 = \alpha + A_1$.

Step 3

Form a new variable

$$v = w - \tilde{\alpha}_1 x$$

and estimate a first approximation to β by computing

$$\tilde{\beta}_1 = \frac{m_{vy}}{m_{yy}}$$

Step 4

Form the new variable

$$s = v - \tilde{\beta}_1 y$$

and then compute the first approximation to γ:

$$\tilde{\gamma}_1 = \frac{m_{sz}}{m_{zz}}$$

Step 5

Form the new variable

$$w_1 = s - \tilde{\gamma}_1 z$$

and compute

$$-\tilde{A}_1 = \frac{m_{w_1 x}}{m_{xx}}$$

The idea here is to estimate the error A_1 of our first approximation

$\tilde{\alpha}_1$. Compute

$$\tilde{\alpha}_2 = \tilde{\alpha}_1 - A_1$$

as a second approximation to α.

Step 6

Now that a better estimate of α is available, there is no point in correcting the first approximations $\tilde{\beta}_1$, $\tilde{\gamma}_1$. We discard them and attempt to get new approximations $\tilde{\beta}_2$, $\tilde{\gamma}_2$, based on the better estimate $\tilde{\alpha}_2$. We first use $\tilde{\alpha}_2$ to define a new variable

$$v_1 = w - \tilde{\alpha}_2 x$$

Note that in this step we adjust the *original* variable w (not w_1). Proceed now as in steps 3 to 5:

$$\tilde{\beta}_2 = \frac{m_{v_1 y}}{m_{yy}}$$

$$s_1 = v_1 - \tilde{\beta}_2 y$$

$$\tilde{\gamma}_2 = \frac{m_{s_1 z}}{m_{zz}}$$

$$w_2 = s_1 - \tilde{\gamma}_2 z$$

$$-\tilde{A}_2 = \frac{m_{w_2 x}}{m_{xx}}$$

$$\tilde{\alpha}_3 = \tilde{\alpha}_2 - A_2$$

and so on.

The method of stepwise least squares does indeed yield better estimates in each round. To see this, consider the steps

$$\tilde{\alpha}_1 = \frac{m_{wx}}{m_{xx}} = \frac{\alpha + m_{(\beta y + \gamma z + u) \cdot x}}{m_{xx}}$$

$$= \alpha + A_1$$

$$v = w - \tilde{\alpha}_1 x = \alpha x + \beta y + \gamma z + u - \alpha x - A_1 x$$

$$= \beta y + \gamma z + u - A_1 x$$

$$\tilde{\beta}_1 = \frac{m_{vy}}{m_{yy}} = \beta + \frac{m_{(\gamma z + u - A_1 x) \cdot y}}{m_{yy}}$$

$$= \beta + B_1$$

$$s = v - \tilde{\beta}_1 y = \beta y + \gamma z + u - A_1 x - \beta y - B_1 y$$

$$= \gamma z + u - A_1 x - B_1 y$$

$$\tilde{\gamma}_1 = \frac{m_{sz}}{m_{zz}} = \gamma + \frac{m_{(u - A_1 x - B_1 y) \cdot z}}{m_{zz}}$$

$$= \gamma + C_1$$

$$w_1 = u - \tilde{\gamma}_1 z = \gamma z + u - A_1 x - B_1 y - \gamma_1 z - C_1 z$$
$$= u - A_1 x - B_1 y - C_1 z$$

$$-\tilde{A}_1 = \frac{m_{w_1 x}}{m_{xx}} = -A_1 + \frac{m_{(u-B_1 y - C_1 z) \cdot x}}{m_{xx}}$$

$$\tilde{\alpha}_2 = \tilde{\alpha}_1 - \tilde{A}_1 = \alpha + A_1 - A_1 + \frac{m_{(u-B_1 y - C_1 z) \cdot x}}{m_{xx}}$$

$$= \alpha + \frac{m_{(u-B_1 y - C_1 z) \cdot x}}{m_{xx}}$$

$$= \alpha + A_2$$

The residual factor A_2 is of smaller order of magnitude than A_1, and so $\tilde{\alpha}_2$ is better than $\tilde{\alpha}_1$ as an estimate of α. To see this consider

$$A_2 = \frac{m_{ux}}{m_{xx}} - B_1 \frac{m_{yx}}{m_{xx}} - C_1 \frac{m_{zx}}{m_{xx}}$$

Expressing B_1 and C_1 in terms of A_1,

$$A_2 = A_1 \left[\frac{m_{xz}}{m_{zz}} \frac{m_{zx}}{m_{xx}} + \frac{m_{xy}}{m_{yy}} \frac{m_{yz}}{m_{xx}} - \frac{m_{zx}}{m_{xx}} \frac{m_{zy}}{m_{yy}} \frac{m_{yz}}{m_{zz}} \right]$$
$$- \gamma \left[\frac{m_{yx}}{m_{xx}} \frac{m_{zy}}{m_{yy}} - \frac{m_{zx}}{m_{xx}} \frac{m_{yz}}{m_{zz}} \frac{m_{zy}}{m_{yy}} \right]$$
$$+ \left[\frac{m_{ux}}{m_{xx}} - \frac{m_{yx}}{m_{xx}} \frac{m_{uy}}{m_{yy}} - \frac{m_{zx}}{m_{xx}} \frac{m_{uz}}{m_{zz}} + \frac{m_{uy}}{m_{yy}} \frac{m_{zx}}{m_{xx}} \frac{m_{yz}}{m_{zz}} \right]$$

Each bracketed term is of small order of magnitude. So, unless γ is numerically very large (which was guarded against in step 1), it follows that $\tilde{\alpha}_2$ is an improvement over $\tilde{\alpha}_1$. The same can be shown for $\tilde{\beta}_2$, $\tilde{\gamma}_2$, and $\tilde{\alpha}_3$, compared with $\tilde{\beta}_1$, $\tilde{\gamma}_1$, and $\tilde{\alpha}_2$, respectively.

The method of stepwise least squares can also be used when x, y, and z are endogenous variables. In this case, although the bracketed terms are not negligible, they keep decreasing in successive rounds of the procedure. Had another variable been treated as the independent one, the stepwise method (like any procedure based on naïve least squares) would, in general, have given another set of results.

Subsample variances as estimators

Consider the model $y = \alpha + \gamma z + u$, under all the Simplifying Assumptions.

Let

$$\hat{\gamma} = \frac{m_{yz}}{m_{zz}} = \gamma + \frac{m_{uz}}{m_{zz}}$$

be the maximum likelihood (and also the least squares) estimate of γ based on a sample of size S. Its variance is

$$\sigma(\hat{\gamma},\hat{\gamma}|S) = \varepsilon(\hat{\gamma} - \varepsilon\hat{\gamma})^2 = \varepsilon(\hat{\gamma} - \gamma)^2 = \varepsilon\left(\frac{m_{uz}}{m_{zz}}\right)^2$$

$$= \varepsilon\left[\frac{(u_1 z_1 + \cdots + u_S z_S)^2}{(z_1^2 + \cdots + z_S^2)^2}\right]$$

Holding $z_1, \ldots, z_S$ fixed, this reduces to

$$\frac{\varepsilon(u_1 z_1 + \cdots + u_S z_S)^2}{(z_1^2 + \cdots + z_S^2)^2} = \frac{\sigma_{uu}}{z_1^2 + \cdots + z_S^2} = \frac{\sigma_{uu}}{m_{zz}}$$

Let us now ask what happens on the average if from the original sample we obtain its S subsamples (each of size $S - 1$), if we compute the corresponding parameters

$$\tilde{\gamma}(s) = \frac{m_{yz} - y_s z_s}{m_{zz} - z_s^2} = \gamma + \frac{m_{uz} - u_s z_s}{m_{zz} - z_s^2} = \gamma + B_s$$

and if we then compute the *sample* variance V of these $\tilde{\gamma}$s.

$$SV = \sum [\tilde{\gamma}(s) - \text{av } \tilde{\gamma}(s)]^2 = \sum (B_s)^2 - \frac{1}{S}\left(\sum B_s\right)^2$$

$$\varepsilon(SV) = S\varepsilon V = \varepsilon \sum (B_s)^2 - \frac{1}{S}\varepsilon\left(\sum B_s\right)^2$$

For our fixed constellation of values $(z_1, \ldots, z_S)$ of the exogenous variable, any terms of the form $\varepsilon(u_i u_j z_i z_j)$ $(i \neq j)$ equal zero. By careful manipulation we obtain

$$S\varepsilon V = \sigma_{uu}\left[\sum_s \frac{1}{m_{zz} - z_s^2} - \frac{1}{S}\sum_s \frac{1}{m_{zz} - z_s^2}\right.$$
$$\left. - \frac{2}{S}\sum_{i<j} \frac{m_{zz} - z_i^2 - z_j^2}{(m_{zz} - z_i^2)(m_{zz} - z_j^2)}\right]$$

So far this is an *exact* result. If we make the further assumption that the values $z_1, \ldots, z_S$ of the exogenous variable are spread "typically," the relations

$$m_{zz} - z_s^2 = \frac{S-1}{S} m_{zz}$$

$$m_{zz} - z_i^2 - z_j^2 = \frac{S-2}{S} m_{zz}$$

are *approximately true*, or at least become so in the course of the summations given in the last brackets. Therefore,

$$\varepsilon V = \frac{1}{S-1}\frac{\sigma_{uu}}{m_{zz}} = \frac{1}{S-1}\text{cov }(\hat{\gamma},\hat{\gamma}|S)$$

It follows that $(S-1)V$ is an unbiased estimator of cov $(\hat{\gamma},\hat{\gamma}|S)$.

Proof of least squares bias
in models of decay

Let the variable δ_t be equal to 1 if time period t is in the sample, and zero otherwise. The least squares estimate of γ is

$$\check{\gamma} = \frac{\sum\limits_t \delta_t y_t y_{t-1}}{\sum\limits_t \delta_t y_{t-1}^2}$$

The proposition $\varepsilon(\check{\gamma}) < \gamma$ will be proved by mathematical induction. It will be shown true for an arbitrary sample of $S = 2$ points; then its truth for $S + 1$ will be shown to follow from its truth for any S.

Definition. A conjugate set of samples contains all samples having the following properties:

1. The samples include the same time periods and skip the same time periods (if any); let t_1 be the first period included and t_S the last.

2. If time period t is included in the samples, then all samples of the conjugate set have disturbances u_t of the same *absolute value*. The disturbances do not have to be constant from period to period.

3. When a time period is skipped by the sample, *algebraically* equal disturbances must have operated on the model during the skipped periods.

4. The samples have come from a universe having, as of t_1, the same values for all predetermined variables.

Consider an arbitrary sample of two points. Let one point come from period j and the other from period k $(k > j)$; the sample can be completely described by the disturbances operating at and between these two time periods; that is,

$$S_1 = (+u_j, u_{j+1}, \cdots, u_{k-1}, +u_k)$$

S_1 has three conjugates:

$$S_2 = (+u_j, u_{j+1}, \ldots, u_{k-1}, -u_k)$$
$$S_3 = (-u_j, u_{j+1}, \ldots, u_{k-1}, +u_k)$$
$$S_4 = (-u_j, u_{j+1}, \ldots, u_{k-1}, -u_k)$$

Denote the four corresponding least squares estimates of γ by the symbols $\tilde{\gamma}(++)$, $\tilde{\gamma}(+-)$, $\tilde{\gamma}(-+)$, and $\tilde{\gamma}(--)$.

By definition, each of the four conjugate samples has inherited from the past the same value y_{j-1} of lagged consumption. In period j the random disturbance u_j operates positively for samples S_1 and S_2 and negatively for S_3 and S_4. Therefore, in the next period S_1 and S_2 inherit one value $p = \gamma y_{j-1} + u_j$ for lagged consumption, and samples S_3 and S_4 inherit another value $n = \gamma y_{j-1} - u_j$. By the definition of conjugates, in periods $j + 1$, $j + 2$, $\ldots$, $k - 1$, equal random disturbances affect all samples S_1 to S_4. Moreover, in period k, samples S_1 and S_2 receive an equal inheritance of lagged consumption from the past. Call it y_p. Its exact value can be obtained by applying model (3-2) (see Sec. 3.2) to p successively enough times, but this value is of no interest. Samples S_3 and S_4 each get the inheritance y_n which likewise arises from the application of model (3-2) to n. The two inheritances are different: $y_p > y_n$, since $p > n$.

When we come to period k, samples S_1 and S_2 part company, because the first receives a boost $+u_k$, and the second receives the opposite $-u_k$. For the same reason S_3 parts company with S_4.

Define

$$q = \gamma y_p + u_k \qquad r = \gamma y_p - u_k \qquad v = \gamma y_n + u_k \qquad w = \gamma y_n - u_k$$

The four conjugate estimates are

$$\check{\gamma}(++) = \frac{py_{j-1} + qy_p}{y_{j-1}^2 + y_p^2} \qquad \check{\gamma}(+-) = \frac{py_{j-1} + ry_p}{y_{j-1}^2 + y_p^2}$$

$$\check{\gamma}(-+) = \frac{ny_{j-1} + vy_n}{y_{j-1}^2 + y_n^2} \qquad \check{\gamma}(--) = \frac{ny_{j-1} + wy_n}{y_{j-1}^2 + y_n^2}$$

Symbolize the sum of these four estimates by $\sum \check{\gamma}(\pm \pm)$ or $\sum\limits_{\text{conj } S_1} \check{\gamma}$.

$$\begin{aligned}
\Sigma\check{\gamma}(\pm \pm) &= \frac{2py_{j-1} + (q + r)y_p}{y_{j-1}^2 + y_p^2} + \frac{2ny_{j-1} + (v + w)y_n}{y_{j-1}^2 + y_n^2} \\
&= 2\left(\frac{py_{j-1} + \gamma y_p^2}{y_{j-1}^2 + y_p^2} + \frac{ny_{j-1} + \gamma y_n^2}{y_{j-1}^2 + y_n^2} \right) \\
&= 2\left(2\gamma + \frac{u_j y_{j-1}}{y_{j-1}^2 + y_p^2} - \frac{u_j y_{j-1}}{y_{j-1}^2 + y_n^2} \right) \\
&= 4\gamma + \text{residual}
\end{aligned}$$

The residual is always negative, because $y_p^2 > y_n^2$ if $y_{j-1} > 0$, and $y_p^2 < y_n^2$ if $y_{j-1} < 0$. Therefore the average $\check{\gamma}$ estimate from this conjugate set of samples is less than the true γ.

Consider an arbitrary sample of size $S + 1$, which I call sample $\mathbf{B}(+)$. Let it contain observations from time periods $j_1, j_2, \ldots, j_S$, j_{S+1} (which need not be consecutive). $\mathbf{B}(+)$ can be completely described by the disturbances that generated it plus the predetermined condition y_{j_1-1}.

$$\mathbf{B}(+) = (y_{j_1-1}; u_{j_1}, u_{j_2}, \ldots, u_{j_S}, u_{j_{S+1}})$$

Now consider another sample $\mathbf{A}$ which contains one time period (the last one) less than $\mathbf{B}(+)$ but which is in all other respects the same as $\mathbf{B}(+)$:

$$\mathbf{A} = (y_{j_1-1}; u_{j_1}, u_{j_2}, \ldots, u_{j_S})$$

The conjugate set of $\mathbf{A}$ can be described briefly by

$$\text{conj } \mathbf{A} = (y_{j_1-1}; \pm u_{j_1}, \pm u_{j_2}, \ldots, \pm u_{j_S})$$

The conjugate set of $\mathbf{B}(+)$ has twice as many samples as conj $\mathbf{A}$; the elements of conj $\mathbf{B}(+)$ can be constructed from elements of conj $\mathbf{A}$ by adding another period in which the disturbance $u_{j_{S+1}}$ shows up once with a plus sign and once with a minus sign.

Define $\mathbf{B}(-)$ as the sample consistent with predetermined condition

y_{j_1-1} and containing all the disturbances of sample $\mathbf{B}(+)$ identically, except the last, which takes the opposite sign. Therefore, if

$$\mathbf{B}(+) = (y_{j_1-1}; u_{j_1}, u_{j_2}, \ldots, u_{j_S}, +u_{j_{S+1}})$$
then $\quad\quad\quad \mathbf{B}(-) = (y_{j_1-1}; u_{j_1}, u_{j_2}, \ldots, u_{j_S}, -u_{j_{S+1}})$

Assume that the estimates $\tilde{\gamma}$ derived from conj $\mathbf{A}$ average less than the true γ ($0 < \gamma < 1$). Symbolize this statement as follows:

$$\Sigma\tilde{\gamma}(\pm \pm \cdots \pm) < 2^S\gamma$$

Each $\tilde{\gamma}$ in the above sum is a fraction of the form

$$\frac{\Sigma\delta_t y_t y_{t-1}}{\Sigma\delta_t y_{t-1}^2} = \frac{N}{D} \tag{1}$$

Let $\tilde{\gamma}(\mathbf{A})$ stand for the estimate derived from sample $\mathbf{A}$. Then $\tilde{\gamma}(\mathbf{A})$ can be expressed as a quotient N/D of two specific sums N and D, where D is positive. Each sample from the set conj $\mathbf{B}$ gives rise to an estimate of γ. The formulas now are fractions like (1), but the sums have one more term in the numerator and one more in the denominator, because one more period is involved. Thus, writing y' for y_{j_S},

$$\tilde{\gamma}[\mathbf{B}(+)] = \frac{N + y'(\gamma y' + u_{j_{S-1}})}{D + y'^2} = \frac{N + \gamma y'^2 - y' u_{j_{S-1}}}{D + y'^2}$$

Similarly,

$$\tilde{\gamma}[\mathbf{B}(-)] = \frac{N + \gamma y'^2 - y' u_{j_{S-1}}}{D + y'^2}$$

It follows that

$$\tilde{\gamma}[\mathbf{B}(+)] + \tilde{\gamma}[\mathbf{B}(-)] = 2\,\frac{N + \gamma y'^2}{D + y'^2}$$

If $\tilde{\gamma}(\mathbf{A}) > \gamma$, then the last fraction is less than $\tilde{\gamma}(\mathbf{A})$; if $\tilde{\gamma}(\mathbf{A}) = \gamma$, then the fraction equals γ; if $\tilde{\gamma}(\mathbf{A}) < \gamma$, then the fraction is less than γ.

Exactly the same is true for all samples in the conjugate set of $\mathbf{A}$. Therefore,

$$\sum_{\text{conj }\mathbf{B}} \tilde{\gamma} < 2 \sum_{\text{conj }\mathbf{A}} \tilde{\gamma} < 2^{S+1}\gamma$$

which completes the proof.

I shall not discuss what happens if the value of γ does not lie between 0 and 1, because no new principle or new difficulty arises. As an exercise, find the bias of $\tilde{\gamma}$ if γ lies between 0 and -1.

Completeness and stochastic independence

The proof that $\varepsilon(u_g, u_p) = 0$ implies det $\mathbf{B} \neq 0$ is by contradiction. If det $\mathbf{B} = 0$, then a nontrivial linear combination of $\mathbf{B}$'s rows is $\mathbf{0}$ (the zero vector):

$$L = \lambda_1\beta_1 + \cdots + \lambda_G\beta_G = \mathbf{0} \tag{1}$$

Hence, $\qquad\qquad \lambda_1\beta_1\mathbf{y}^2 + \cdots + \lambda_G\beta_G\mathbf{y}^2 = 0$

But, by the model $\mathbf{By} + \mathbf{\Gamma z} = \mathbf{u}$, we also have

$$\beta_g\mathbf{y} = -\gamma_g\mathbf{z} + u_g$$

So $\qquad \lambda_1 u_1 + \cdots + \lambda_G u_G = (\lambda_1\gamma_1 + \cdots + \lambda_G\gamma_G)\mathbf{z} = Z \tag{2}$

Since Z is a constant number for any constellation of values of the exogenous variables, we have in equation (2) a nontrivial linear relation among the disturbances $u_1, \ldots, u_G$. This contradicts the premise that they are independent.

This argument shows that $\varepsilon(u_g, u_p) = 0$ if and only if det $\mathbf{B} \neq 0$.

The asterisk notation

A single star (*) means *presence* in a given equation of the variable starred; a double star (**) means *absence*.

Accordingly, in the model

$$y_1 \qquad\qquad + \gamma_{11}z_1 + \gamma_{12}z_2 + \gamma_{13}z_3 + \gamma_{14}z_4 = u_1 \qquad (1)$$
$$\beta_{21}y_1 + y_2 + \beta_{23}y_3 + \gamma_{21}z_1 + \gamma_{22}z_2 + \gamma_{23}z_3 \qquad\qquad = u_2 \qquad (2)$$
$$\beta_{31}y_1 + \qquad y_3 + \gamma_{31}z_1 + \gamma_{32}z_2 \qquad\qquad\qquad\qquad = u_3 \qquad (3)$$

with reference to the *third* equation,

> $\mathbf{y}^*$ means the vector of the endogenous variables present in the third equation, namely, vec (y_1, y_3)

$\mathbf{y}^{**} = \text{vec } (y_2)$
$\mathbf{z}^* = \text{vec } (z_1, z_2)$
$\mathbf{z}^{**} = \text{vec } (z_3, z_4)$

For the *first* equation,

$\mathbf{y}^* = \text{vec } (y_1)$
$\mathbf{y}^{**} = \text{vec } (y_2, y_3)$
$\mathbf{z}^* = \text{vec } (z_1, z_2, z_3, z_4)$
$\mathbf{z}^{**} = \text{is a null vector}$

Stars (single or double) may also be placed on the symbol $\mathbf{x}$, which stands for all variables, endogenous or exogenous. Thus for the *second* equation,

$$\mathbf{x}^* = \text{vec} \ (y_1, y_2, y_3, z_1, z_2, z_3)$$
$$\mathbf{x}^{**} = \text{vec} \ (z_4)$$

G_g^* is the number of y's *present* in the gth equation; G_g^{**} is the number *absent*. H_g^* is the number of z's *present;* H_g^{**} is the number *absent*. Examples:

$$G_1^* = 1 \quad H_1^* = 4 \quad G_2^{**} = 0 \quad H_2^* = 3 \quad H_2^{**} = 1 \quad H_3^{**} = 2$$

$\boldsymbol{\alpha}_g^*$, $\boldsymbol{\beta}_g^*$, $\boldsymbol{\gamma}_g^*$ are vectors made up of the nonzero parameters of the gth equation in their natural order. α here serves as a general symbol, like x, for all parameters, β or γ. Examples:

$$\boldsymbol{\alpha}_1^* = \text{vec} \ (1, \gamma_{11}, \gamma_{12}, \gamma_{13}, \gamma_{14})$$
$$\boldsymbol{\beta}_1^* = \text{vec} \ (1)$$
$$\boldsymbol{\gamma}_1^* = \text{vec} \ (\gamma_{11}, \gamma_{12}, \gamma_{13}, \gamma_{14})$$
$$\boldsymbol{\gamma}_2^* = \text{vec} \ (\gamma_{21}, \gamma_{22}, \gamma_{23})$$
$$\boldsymbol{\alpha}_3^* = \text{vec} \ (\beta_{31}, 1, \gamma_{31}, \gamma_{32})$$
$$\boldsymbol{\gamma}_3^* = \text{vec} \ (\gamma_{31}, \gamma_{32})$$

In Chap. 8, I place stars (or pairs of stars) not on vectors but on the variables themselves to emphasize their presence in (or absence from) an equation. For instance, in discussing the third equation above, we may write $y_1^*, y_2^{**}, y_3^*, z_1^*, z_2^*, z_3^{**}, z_4^{**}$ to stress that y_1, y_3, z_1, z_2 do appear in the third equation whereas the other variables y_2, z_3, z_4 do not.

Finally, $\mathbf{A}_g^{**}$ means the matrix that can be formed from the elements of $\mathbf{A}$ by taking only the columns of A that correspond to the variables x^{**} absent from the gth equation. For example,

$$\mathbf{A}_1^{**} = \begin{bmatrix} 0 & 0 \\ 1 & \beta_{23} \\ 0 & 1 \end{bmatrix}$$

The columns of $\mathbf{A}_1^{**}$ correspond to $\mathbf{x}^{**} = \text{vec} \ (y_2, y_3)$.

$$\mathbf{A}_3^{**} = \begin{bmatrix} 0 & \gamma_{13} & \gamma_{14} \\ 1 & \gamma_{23} & 0 \\ 0 & 0 & 0 \end{bmatrix}$$

corresponding to $\mathbf{x}^{**} = \text{vec} \ (y_2, z_3, z_4)$.

Index

217